International Directory
of
Historical Clothing

by

Irene Pennington Huenefeld

The Scarecrow Press, Inc.
Metuchen, N.J.   1967

Preface

This volume is an international directory, listing authentic clothing of various periods and countries found in museums, art galleries, historical societies, libraries and churches, located in Canada, the United States, and Europe.

It is the only directory, national or international, which is devoted exclusively to the listing of authentic clothing collections. Although it is generally known there are many museums which have special sections of historical clothing only on rare occasions are these acquisitions included in directories and indexes of such institutions.

The International Directory of Historical Clothing provides a comprehensive reference on acquisitions of casual, formal, national and regional clothing; military, civil and professional uniforms; and ecclesiastical vestments. These are classified and listed by both century and sex.

Museum research, where clothing of a specific period and country may be studied, photographed, sketched and in some cases even examined, should not only contribute much to effectiveness in the designing of costumes for theatrical productions in the educational and professional theatre, but should also be of considerable value for scholars in opera and theatre history, literature, novel and historical writing, art illustration and dress designing. Since clothing is of great significance in human culture then such a directory should be of interest in the field of anthropology and sociology. It, also, should be of interest to libraries, museums, and historical societies.

The information contained in this volume was collected over a period of six years by means of one or more questionnaires mailed to over 2,000 institutions in Canada, the United States, and Europe. This information was supplemented and enlarged upon by

iii

studying personally the costumes in a number of authentic period costume collections in these countries.

The arrangement of information in this volume is as follows:

Part I is devoted to North American acquisitions and Part II to European acquisitions.

Part I and II each contain the following sub-headings:

A. Lists of institutions alphabetized geographically by country, state or province, and city with the street address included.

B. Lists of institutions alphabetized by title.

C. Clothing and clothing accessories are alphabetized by categories listed as follows:

1. Accessories
2. Armor
3. Ceremonial Clothing
4. Civil Uniforms
5. Ecclesiastical Vestments
6. Formal and Casual Clothing
7. Headdresses
8. Historical Clothing
9. Jewelry
10. Military Uniforms and Accessories
11. National and Regional Clothing
12. Professional Uniforms

A condensed clothing code can be found at the beginning of each category except Historical. The Master Code which appears at the beginning of sub-heading C is as follows:

c	-	Century A.D.
B.C.	-	Century B.C.
A	-	Casual Clothing
B	-	Formal Clothing
C	-	Children's Clothing
E	-	Ecclesiastical Vestments
F	-	Female Clothing
H	-	Headdress
J	-	Jewelry

iv

M - Male Clothing

N - National and Regional Clothing

P - Professional Uniforms

S - Accessories

T - Civil Uniforms

U - Unclassified Clothing as to century

X - Military Uniforms

Y - Armor

Z - Ceremonial Clothing

An example of the usage of the code under a specific category is as follows:

A scholar in Boston, Massachusetts searching for authentic church vestments of the 16th century would find by referring to the category Ecclesiastical Vestments one museum in Boston with examples of these vestments. The information would be listed as:

Museum of Fine Arts, Boston, Mass.
cf. p. 16;16c; B-M, 17c; B-M, 19c; B-M, 20; B-M

By further checking in the same category he would find in nearby Deerfield, Massachusetts there are acquisitions of church vestments, however, the earliest one recorded is in the 18th century, as shown below:

Dwight-Barnard House, Deerfield, Mass.
cf. p.16; 18c; B-M, 19c; B-M, 20c; B-M

When "cf. p.___" appears, as in the above example, it refers to the page citation in the geographical listing (see p. 13-22) which gives the full street address of the museum or institution.

Many of the questionnaires returned included historical information not requested but which should be of value to a number of scholars. This material is not given by code but is presented almost verbatim as quoted by a representative of the institution. An example from Part I is as follows:

Eighteenth Century
British uniform taken from a soldier in the

battle at Ridgefield, Connecticut in 1777.

Danbury Scott-Fanton Museum and Historical Society, Danbury, Conn.

D. Costume Terms in Part I are listed alphabetically under the following headings:

1. Accessories
2. Childrens' Clothing
3. Ecclesiastical Vestments
4. Footwear
5. Headdress
6. Lingerie
7. Men's Clothing
8. Military Uniforms
9. Neckwear
10. Organizational Uniforms
11. Over Garments
12. Professional Uniforms
13. Sport Clothing
14. Women's Clothing

An example is the term Widow's Weeds which is alphabetized in Part I under the heading Women's Clothing and described as:

Widow's Weeds--women's evening gowns:

Rochester Museum of Arts and Sciences, Rochester, N. Y.

cf. p. 19   19c

Costume Terms in Part II are listed alphabetically under the following headings:

1. Accessories
2. Armor
3. Childrens' Clothing
4. Ecclesiastical Vestments
5. Footwear
6. Headdress
7. Jewelry

8. Men's Clothing

9. Military Uniforms

10. Outer Garments

11. Women's Clothing

An example is the term <u>Rajput Warrior</u> which is alphabetized in <u>Part II</u> under the heading <u>Military Uniforms</u> and described as:

> Rajput Warrior's full war panoply -
> helmet, boots, cuirass "of the four
> mirrors," coat "of a thousand eyes,"
> vambrace, pouch, and sword:
> Wallace Collection, London, England
> cf. p.99 16c

I wish to express my appreciation for the assistance given me by museum personnel in answering the questionnaires and to those who generously gave of their time when I personally visited their institution. My sincere thanks goes to four of my colleagues at Louisiana State University, Drs. Waldo W. Braden, Giles W. Gray, Owen M. Peterson, Claude L. Shaver and to my daughter, Johanne, for encouragement in this endeavor. I am indebted to Johanne and to Bill Brumbalow a former student of mine, who now teaches at the University of Maryland, for valuable assistance in proof reading.

Table of Contents

PART ONE

North America

Institutions
Arranged
Geographically

Institutions - Arranged Geographically

Canada
British Columbia
Esquimalt
  Maritime Museum of British Columbia, Esquimalt Road
Kamloops
  Kamloops Museum Association, 207 Seymour Street
Prince Rupert
  Museum of Northern British Columbia
Vedder Crossing
  Royal Canadian Engineers Museum, Camp Chilliwack

Ontario
Hamilton
  Dundurn Castle Museum, Dundurn Park
Kitchener
  Waterloo Historical Society Museum, 58 Queen Street, N.
Napanee
  Lennox and Addington County Museum, 41 Dundas Street, W.
Niagara Falls
  Niagara Falls Museum, Ltd., 1651 River Road
Toronto 5
  Royal Ontario Museum, 100 Queen's Park

Quebec
Montreal
  Notre Dame Church, 116 W. Notre Dame Street
Quebec
  Musée de la Province, Parc des Champs de Bataille

United States
Alabama
Birmingham
  Arlington Historical Society, 331 Cotton Ave., S. W.

Fort McClellan
  Edith Nourse Rogers Museum, United States Women's Army Corps Center
Mobile
  Historic Mobile Preservation Society, 350 Oakleigh Place
Montgomery
  First White House of the Confederacy, Washington and Union Streets

  Montgomery Museum of Fine Arts, 440 South McDonough Street

  State of Alabama, Department of Archives and History

Arizona
Flagstaff
  Museum of Northern Arizona, Northern Arizona Society of Science and Art, Fort Valley Road
Moccasin
  Pipe Spring National Monument
Prescott
  Sharlot Hall, Historical Museum of Arizona, West Gurley
Tucson
  Arizona Pioneers' Historical Society, 949 East Second Street

  Arizona State Museum, University of Arizona

  University of Arizona Art Gallery, Speedway at Palm Road

California
Imperial
  Imperial County Pioneer Museum
Long Beach
  La Casa de Rancho, Los

13

Cerritos, 4600 Virginia Road
Los Angeles
   Los Angeles County Museum,
   Exposition Park (7)

   Southwest Museum, 10 High-
   land Park
Oakland
   Oakland Public Museum, 1426
   Oak Street
Pasadena
   Pasadena Art Museum, 46
   North Los Robles Avenue
San Francisco
   M. H. De Young Memorial
   Museum, Golden Gate Park
   (18)
San Jose
   Rosicrucian Art Gallery,
   Rosicrucian Park
Santa Ana
   Charles W. Bowers Memorial
   Museum, 2002 North Main
   Street
Stockton
   Pioneer Museum and Haggin
   Galleries, Victory Park,
   Pershing Avenue (3)

Colorado
Boulder
   Boulder Pioneer Museum,
   1655 Broadway Avenue
Denver
   Denver Art Museum, 1343
   Acoma

   State Museum, The State
   Historical Society of Colorado,
   East 14th Avenue at Sherman
Rocky Ford
   Rocky Ford Museum
   Tenth Street

Connecticut
Clinton
   Stanton House
Colebrook
   Colebrook Historical Society,
   Colebrook Town Hall
Danbury
   Danbury Scott-Fanton Museum
   and Historical Society, Inc.,
   43 Main Street

Hartford
   Connecticut Historical Society,
   1 Elizabeth Street

   Wadsworth Atheneum, 25
   Atheneum Square North
Madison
   Madison Historical Society,
   Boston Post Road
Mystic
   Marine Historical Association,
   Inc., Greenmanville Avenue
New Haven
   New Haven Colony Historical
   Society, 114 Whitney Avenue
New London
   Lyman Allyn Museum, 100
   Mohegan Avenue
New Milford
   New Milford Historical Society,
   55 Main Street
Norwich
   Slater Memorial Museum, The
   Norwich Free Academy, 108
   Crescent Street
Wallingford
   Pond Hill Farm
Washington
   Gunn Memorial Library Muse-
   um, Washington Green
Wilton
   Craft Center Museum, Inc.,
   80 Danbury Road

Delaware
Dover
   Delaware State Museum, 316
   South Governors Avenue
Winterthur
   Henry Francis du Pont Winter-
   thur Museum

District of Columbia
Washington, D. C.
   Copp Costume Collection,
   Smithsonian Institution, Arts
   and Industries Bldg.

   Folger Museum

   Hall of American Costume,
   Smithsonian Institution

   Museum, National Society,
   Daughters of the American

14

Revolution, 1776 D Street, N. W.

National Air Museum, Smithsonian Institution, Independence Avenue at Tenth St., N. W.

Red Cross National Headquarters Museum, 17th Street between D and E Streets

Textile Museum, 2320 S Street, N. W.

United States National Museum, Costume Division, Smithsonian Institution, Arts and Industries Bldg.

United States Women's Army Corps Museum

Florida

Gainesville
Florida State Museum, University of Florida, Seagle Bldg.

St. Petersburg
St. Petersburg Historical Museum, 335 Second Avenue, N. E.

Sarasota
John and Mable Ringling Museum of Art, 5401 Bay Shore Road
Ringling Circus Museum

Stuart
House of Refuge Museum, Hutchinson Island

Tavares
Lake County Historical Society, 315 New Hampshire Avenue

Georgia

Atlanta
Atlanta Art Association Galleries, 1280 Peachtree Street, N. E.

Fort Benning
United States Army Infantry Museum, Building 1234

Hawaii

Honolulu
Hawaiian Mission Children's Society, 553 South King Street

Illinois

Aurora
Aurora Historical Society, Inc., 304 Oak Avenue

Belvidere
Boone County Historical Society, 705 John Street

Chicago
Chicago Historical Society, North Avenue and Clark Street

George F. Harding Museum, 4835 South Lake Park Avenue

Evanston
Rest Cottage, 1730 Chicago Avenue

Vandalia
Vandalia Historical Society Museum, 212 Gallatin Avenue

Wilmette
Wilmette Historical Commission, Village Hall

Winnetka
Winnetka Historical Society, 516 Walnut Street

Indiana

Fort Wayne
Allen County-Fort Wayne Historical Museum, 1424 West Jefferson Street

Kokomo
Howard County Historical Society, Courthouse

Rushville
Rush County Historical Society, 619 North Perkins

South Bend
Northern Indiana Historical Society, 112 South Lafayette Blvd.

Terre Haute
Historical Museum of Wabash Valley, 1411 South Sixth Street

Sheldon Swope Art Gallery, 25 South Seventh Street

Iowa

Davenport
Davenport Public Museum 704 Brady Street

Decorah
  Norwegian-American Historical
  Museum, Luther College, 520
  West Water Street

Kansas
Fort Scott
  Old Fort Historical Museum,
  101 Blair Avenue
Manhatten
  Riley County Historical Museum,
  Memorial Auditorium Building,
  110 Poyntz Avenue

Kentucky
Bowling Green
  Kentucky Museum and Library,
  Western Kentucky State Col-
  lege
Lexington
  Ashland, East Main and
  Sycamore Road
Paris
  Duncan Tavern Historic Center,
  Public Square
Richmond
  College Memorial Museum,
  Eastern Kentucky State Col-
  lege, Lancaster Avenue

Louisiana
New Orleans
  Louisiana State Museum
  Jackson Square

Maine
Brunswick
  Pejepscot Historical Society,
  12 School Street
Farmington
  Nordica Homestead
Kennebunk
  Brick Store Museum, 117
  Maine Street
Poland Spring
  Shaker Colony Museum,
  Sabbathday Lake
Saco
  York Institute, Main Street
York
  Society for the Preservation
  of Historic Landmarks in
  York County, Inc., Old School

House

Maryland
Baltimore
  Baltimore Museum of Art,
  Cone Textile Collection,
  Wyman Park

  Lovely Lane Museum of the
  Baltimore Conference Metho-
  dist Historical Society, 2200
  South Paul Street

  Maryland Historical Society,
  201 West Monument Street

  Walters Art Gallery, Charles
  and Centre Streets
Oakland
  Garrett County Historical Society, Second Street

Massachusetts
Beverly
  Beverly Historical Society,
  117 Cabot Street
Boston
  Bostonian Society, Old State
  House, 206 Washington Street

  Harrison Gray Otis House,
  141 Cambridge Street

  Museum of Fine Arts, 469
  Huntington Avenue

  Society for the Preservation
  of New England Antiquities,
  141 Cambridge Street
Cambridge
  Fogg Art Museum, Harvard
  University

  Harvard College Library
Deerfield
  Dwight-Barnard House
Hadley
  Porter-Phelps-Hungtington
  Historic House Museum, 128
  River Drive
New Bedford
  The Whaling Museum, 18
  Johnny Cake Hill
Northampton
  Northampton Historical Socie-
  ty Museum, Memorial Hall,
  240 Main Street

16

Plymouth
  Pilgrim Hall, Court Street

Plymouth Antiquarian Society,
  Warren Avenue
Salem
  Essex Institute, 132 Essex
  Street
Sturbridge
  Old Sturbridge Village
Wenham
  Wenham Historical Associa-
  tion and Museum, Inc., Main
  Street
Worcester
  John Woodman Higgins Armory,
  Inc., 100 Barber Avenue

  Worcester Historical Society,
  39 Salisbury Street

Michigan
Ann Arbor
  Washtenaw Historical Society,
  1209 South State Street
Detroit
  Detroit Historical Museum,
  5401 Woodward Street

  Detroit Institute of Arts, 5200
  Woodward Avenue
East Lansing
  Michigan State University
  Museum

Minnesota
Anoka
  Anoka County Historical So-
  ciety, Courthouse
Glenwood
  Pope County Historical Soci-
  ety, Courthouse
Moorhead
  Clay County Historical Soci-
  ety, Clay County Courthouse
Rochester
  Olmsted County Historical
  Society, 214 Third Avenue,
  S. W.
Saint Paul
  Minnesota Historical Society
  Museum, Cedar Street and
  Central Avenue
Slayton

Murray County Historical
Society

Mississippi
Biloxi
  Jefferson Davis Shrine and
  Museum, West Beach
Oxford
  Mary Buie Museum, 510
  University Avenue
Pascagoula
  Spanish Fort and Museum, 200
  Fort Street
Vicksburg
  Old Court House Museum

Missouri
Jefferson City
  Cole County Historical Society,
  109 Madison
Kansas City
  Kansas City Museum Associa-
  tion, 3218 Gladstone Blvd.

  Liberty Memorial, 100 West
  26th Street

  William Rockhill Nelson Gallery
  of Art, 4525 Oak Street
Kirksville
  E. M. Violette Museum, North
  East Missouri State College
St. Louis
  Campbell House Museum, 1508
  Locust Street

  City Art Museum of St. Louis,
  Forest Park

  Concordia Historical Institute,
  801 DeMun Avenue

  Missouri Historical Society,
  Jefferson Memorial Bldg.,
  Lindell at DeBaliviere

Montana
Browning
  Museum of the Plains Indian
Virginia City
  Virginia City-Madison County
  Historical Museum

Nebraska
Chadron
  Museum of the Fur Trade

17

Lincoln
 Nebraska State Historical
 Society, 1500 R Street

Nevada
Carson City
 Nevada State Museum
Reno
 Nevada Historical Society,
 P. O. Box 1129

New Hampshire
Canterbury
 Shaker Colony Museum
Concord
 New Hampshire Historical
 Society, 30 Park Street
Manchester
 Manchester Historic Associa-
 tion, 129 Amherst Street
Peterborough
 Goyette Museum of Americana,
 Elm Street
Portsmouth
 John Paul Jones House, 43
 Middle Street

New Jersey
Camden
 Camden County Historical
 Society, Euclid Avenue and
 Park Blvd.
Montclair
 Montclair Art Museum,
 Bloomfield and South
 Mountain Avenues
Morristown
 Morristown National Histor-
 ical Park, P. O. Box 759
Newark
 New Jersey Historical Soci-
 ety Museum, 230 Broadway
Nutley
 Nutley Historical Society
 Museum, 65 Church Street
Ridgewood
 Paramus Historical and
 Preservation Society, 650
 East Glen Avenue
Springfield
 Springfield Historical Society,
 126 Morris Avenue

New Mexico
Santa Fe
 Anthropology Division, Muse-
 um of New Mexico, Camino
 Lejo

 Museum of International Folk
 Art, Museum of New Mexico,
 Pecos Road

 Museum of Navajo Ceremonial
 Art, Camino Lejo

 Museum of New Mexico,
 Division of History, Palace
 Avenue
University Park
 New Mexico State University
 Museum

New York
Albany
 Museum of Art, New York
 State Education Building
Batavia
 Holland Land Office Museum,
 131 West Main Street
Brooklyn
 Brooklyn Museum, 188 Eastern
 Parkway
Buffalo
 Buffalo Museum of Science,
 Humboldt Park
Canton
 History Center of St. Law-
 rence County, Courthouse
Cooperstown
 Farmers' Museum, New York
 State Historical Association

 Fenimore Home, New York
 Historical Association

 National Baseball Hall of
 Fame and Museum, Inc.,
 Main Street
Crestwood
 American Museum of Comedy,
 161 Westchester Avenue
East Hampton, L. I.
 East Hampton Historical
 Society, Main Street
East Meadow, L. I.
 Nassau County Historical Mu-
 seum, Nassau County Park

Fort Plain
 Tryon County Muzzle Loaders, Inc., Fort K Lock
Ithaca
 DeWitt Historical Society of Tompkins County, Inc., 113 East Court Street
New York City
 American Museum of Natural History, Central Park West at 79th Street

 Costume Institute, Metropolitan Museum of Art, Fifth Avenue at 82nd Street

 Lotos Club, 5 East 66th Street

 Metropolitan Museum of Art, Fifth Avenue at 82nd Street

 Museum for the Arts of Decoration, Cooper Union for the Advancement of Science and Art, Cooper Square at 7th Street

 Museum of the American Indian, Heye Foundation, Broadway at 155th Street

 Museum of the City of New York, 1220 Fifth Avenue

 Traphagen School of Fashion, Museum Collection, 1680 Broadway
North Salem
 Hammond Museum, Inc., Deveau Road
Ogdensburg
 Remington Art Memorial, 303 Washington Street
Old Chatham
 Shaker Museum
Orient, Long Island
 Oysterponds Historical Society, Inc., Village Lane
Ossining
 Ossining Historical Society Museum, 83 Croton Avenue
Rochester
 Rochester Historical Society, 485 East Avenue

 Rochester Museum of Arts and Sciences, 657 East Avenue
Staten Island
 Staten Island Italian Historical Society, 75 Stuyvesant Place
Tarrytown
 Sleepy Hollow Restorations, Westchester County, Route 9
Ticonderoga
 Fort Ticonderoga, Juno 7072
Warsaw
 Warsaw Historical Society, 15 Perry Avenue
Waterloo
 Waterloo Library and Historical Society
West Point
 West Point Museum, United States Military Academy

Wyoming
 Middlebury Historical Society
  North Carolina
Greensboro
 Greensboro Historical Museum, 220 Church Street

 Guilford Courthouse National Military Park, New Garden Road, Box 9145, Plaza Station
Raleigh
 Hall of History, Corner of Edentown and Salisbury Street, P. O. Box 1881
Wilmington
 New Hanover County Museum, County Courthouse
  North Dakota
Fargo
 North Dakota Institute, North Dakota Agricultural College Campus
Valley City
 Barnes County Historical Museum, Courthouse
  Ohio
Cincinnati
 Cincinnati Art Museum, Eden Park
Cleveland
 Cleveland Public Library, 325 Superior Avenue

Western Reserve Historical
Society, 10825 East Blvd.
Columbus
Ohio State Museum, High
Street at 15th Avenue
Dayton
Air Force Museum, Wright-
Patterson Air Force Base
Elyria
Lorain County Historical So-
ciety Museum, 334 Washing-
ton Avenue
Greenville
Darke County Historical
Society and Garst Museum,
223 West Third Street
Lima
Allen County Museum, 620
West Market Street
Marietta
Campus Martius Museum, 601
Second Street
Oberlin
Oberlin College Art Museum
Shaker Heights
Shaker Historical Society,
Moreland School of our City
of Shaker Heights, 12931
Shaker Heights

Oklahoma
Ponca City
Ponca City Indian Museum,
Ponca City Library Bldg.,
408 South Seventh Street
Tulsa
Philbrook Art Center, 2727
South Rockford Road

Oregon
Hood River
Hood River County Historical
Museum, County Courthouse
Jacksonville
Jacksonville Museum, 206
North Fifth Street, P. O.
Box 85
Portland
Oregon Historical Society,
235 S. W. Market Street

Pennsylvania
Easton
Northampton County Historical
and Genealogical Society, 101
South Fourth Street

Erie
Erie Public Museum, 356
West 6th Street
Lancaster
Lancaster County Historical
Society, 230 North President
Avenue

Pennsylvania Farm Museum
of Landis Valley, Kissel Hill
Road
Mercer
Mercer County Historical So-
ciety, 119 South Pitt Street
Philadelphia
Friends Meeting House, Fourth
and Arch Street

Philadelphia Museum of Art,
Benjamin Franklin Parkway
at Twenty-Sixth Street

University Museum, University
of Pennsylvania, 33rd and
Spruce Street
Pittsburg
Carnegie Museum, Carnegie
Institute, 4400 Forbes Avenue
Swarthmore
Swarthmore College, Friends
Historical Library
York
Historical Society of York
County, 250 East Market
Street

Rhode Island
Kingston
University of Rhode Island,
Textiles and Clothing Depart-
ment
Newport
Newport Historical Society, 82
Truro Street

Preservation Society of New-
port County, Washington
Square
Portsmouth
Portsmouth Historical Society
Providence
Costume Center, Museum of
Art, Rhode Island School of
Design, 224 Benefit Street

Wickford
Smith's Castle, Cocumscussoc
Association

South Carolina
Charleston
Charleston Museum, 125
Rutledge Avenue

South Dakota
Sioux Falls
Pettigrew Museum, 131 North
Duluth Avenue

Tennessee
Nashville
Tennessee State Museum, War
Memorial Bldg., Capitol Blvd.

Texas
Austin
Texas Memorial Museum, 24th
and Trinity
Dallas
Dallas Historical Society, Hall
of State, Fair Park
Denton
Museum of Historic Costumes,
Texas Woman's University
Houston
San Jacinto Monument and Mu-
seum
San Antonio
Alamo

Witte Memorial Museum, 3801
Broadway, Brackenridge Park
Waco
Heritage Society of Waco,
Mill Street and Brazos River

Vermont
Bennington
Bennington Museum, West
Main Street
Burlington
Robert Hull Fleming Museum,
University of Vermont

Virginia
Boydton
Roanoke River Museum
Fort Lee
Quartermaster Museum,

United States Army Quarter-
master Corps
Fredericksburg
James Monroe Law Office
and Museum
Natural Bridge
Museum of Motoring Memories,
P. O. Box 115, U. S. Route
11
Norfolk
Norfolk Museum of Arts and
Sciences, Yarmouth Street
at the Hague
Richmond
Confederate Museum, 1201
East Clay Street

Valentine Museum, 1015 East
Clay Street
Williamsburg
Colonial Williamsburg, Inc.,
P. O. Box 516, Goodwin
Building

Washington
Olympia
State Capitol Historical Mu-
seum, 211 West 21st Street
Port Townsend
Jefferson County Historical
Museum, City Hall
Seattle
Museum of History and Indus-
try, 2720 Lake Washington
Blvd., North

Seattle Art Museum, Volunteer
Park

University of Washington,
Home Economics Department

Washington State Museum,
University of Washington, 4037
15th N. E.

Wisconsin
Beloit
Beloit Historical Museum, 220
West Grand Avenue
Green Bay
Neville Public Museum, 129
South Jefferson Street
Kenosha
Kenosha County Historical

21

Museum, County Courthouse

Keshena

Angus F. Lookaround Memorial
Museum, Menominee Indian
Reservation

Madison

State Historical Society of
Wisconsin, 816 State Street

Milwaukee

Milwaukee Public Museum,
818 West Wisconsin Avenue

Oconto

Beyer Home, Oconto County
Historical Museum, 917 Park
Avenue

Wyoming

Cody

Buffalo Bill Museum, Buffalo
Bill Memorial Association

Whitney Gallery of Western
Art

PART I

Institutions

By

Title

United States And Canada

Institutions Arranged by Title

Canada
Dundurn Castle Museum
Hamilton, Ontario

Kamloops Museum Association
Kamloops, British Columbia

Lennox and Addington County
Museum
Napanee, Ontario

Maritime Museum of British
Columbia
Esquimalt, British Columbia

Musée de la Province
Quebec, Quebec

Museum of Northern British
Columbia
Prince Rupert, British Columbia

Niagara Falls Museum, Ltd.
Niagara Falls, Ontario

Notre Dame Church
Montreal, Quebec

Royal Canadian Engineers Museum
Vedder Crossing, British
Columbia

Royal Ontario Museum
Toronto, Ontario

Waterloo Historical Society
Museum
Kitchener, Ontario

United States
Air Force Museum
Wright-Patterson Air Force
Base, Dayton, Ohio

Alamo
San Antonio, Texas

Allen County-Fort Wayne Historical Museum
Fort Wayne, Indiana

Allen County Museum
Lima, Ohio

American Museum of Comedy
Crestwood, New York

American Museum of Natural
History
New York, New York

Anoka County Historical Society
Anoka, Minnesota

Anthropology Division, Museum of
New Mexico
Sante Fe, New Mexico

Angus F. Lookaround Memorial
Museum
Keshena, Wisconsin

Arizona Pioneers' Historical
Society
Tucson, Arizona

Arizona State Museum
Tucson, Arizona

Arlington Historical Society
Birmingham, Alabama

Ashland
Lexington, Kentucky

Atlanta Art Association Galleries
Atlanta, Georgia

Aurora Historical Society, Inc.
Aurora, Illinois

Baltimore Museum of Art
Baltimore, Maryland

Barnes County Historical Museum
Valley City, North Dakota

Beloit Historical Museum
Beloit, Wisconsin

Bennington Museum
Bennington, Vermont

Beverly Historical Society
Beverly, Massachusetts

Beyer Home, Oconto County
Historical Museum
Oconto, Wisconsin

Boone County Historical Society
Belvidere, Illinois

Bostonian Society
Boston, Massachusetts

Boulder Pioneer Museum
Boulder, Colorado

Brick Store Museum
Kennebunk, Maine

Brooklyn Museum
Brooklyn, New York

Buffalo Bill Museum
Cody, Wyoming

Buffalo Museum of Science
Buffalo, New York

Camden County Historical Society
Camden, New Jersey

Campbell House Museum
St. Louis, Missouri

Campus Martius Museum
Marietta, Ohio

Carnegie Museum
Pittsburgh, Pennsylvania

Charleston Museum
Charleston, South Carolina

Charles W. Bowers Memorial
Museum
Santa Ana, California

Chicago Historical Society
Chicago, Illinois

Cincinnati Art Museum
Cincinnati, Ohio

City Art Museum of St. Louis
St. Louis, Missouri

Clay County Historical Society
Moorhead, Minnesota

Cleveland Public Library
Cleveland, Ohio

Colebrook Historical Society
Colebrook, Connecticut

Cole County Historical Society
Jefferson City, Missouri

College Memorial Museum
Richmond, Kentucky

Colonial Williamsburg, Inc.
Williamsburg, Virginia

Concordia Historical Institute
St. Louis, Missouri

Confederate Museum
Richmond, Virginia

Connecticut Historical Society
Hartford, Connecticut

Copp Costume Collection
Smithsonian Institute
Washington, D. C.

Costume Center, Museum of Art,
Rhode Island School of Design
Providence, Rhode Island

Costume Institute, Metropolitan
Museum of Art

New York, New York

Craft Center Museum, Inc.
Wilton, Connecticut

Dallas Historical Society, Hall
of State
Dallas, Texas

Danbury Scott-Fanton Museum
and Historical Society, Inc.
Danbury, Connecticut

Darke County Historical Society
and Garst Museum
Greenville, Ohio

Davenport Public Museum
Davenport, Iowa

Delaware State Museum
Dover, Delaware

Denver Art Museum
Denver, Colorado

Detroit Historical Museum
Detroit, Michigan

Detroit Institute of Arts
Detroit, Michigan

DeWitt Historical Society of
Tompkins County, Inc.
Ithaca, New York

Duncan Tavern Historic Center
Paris, Kentucky

Dwight-Barnard House
Deerfield, Massachusetts

East Hampton Historical Society
East Hampton, Long Island,
New York

Edith Nourse Rogers Museum
Fort McClellan, Alabama

E. M. Violette Museum
Kirksville, Missouri

Erie Public Museum

Erie, Pennsylvania

Essex Institute
Salem, Massachusetts

Farmers' Museum
Cooperstown, New York

Fenimore House
Cooperstown, New York

First White House of the Confederacy
Montgomery, Alabama

Florida State Museum
Gainesville, Florida

Fogg Art Museum
Cambridge, Massachusetts

Folger Museum
Washington, D. C.

Fort Ticonderoga
Ticonderoga, New York

Friends Meeting House
Philadelphia, Pennsylvania

Garrett County Historical Society
Oakland, Maryland

George F. Harding Museum
Chicago, Illinois

Goyette Museum of Americana
Peterborough, New Hampshire

Greensboro Historical Museum
Greensboro, North Carolina

Guilford Courthouse National
Military Park
Greensboro, North Carolina

Gunn Memorial Library Museum
Washington, Connecticut

Hall of American Costume, Smithsonian Institution
Washington, D. C.

Hall of History
Raleigh, North Carolina

Hammond Museum, Inc.
North Salem, New York

Harrison Gray Otis House
Boston, Massachusetts

Harvard College Library
Cambridge, Massachusetts

Hawaiian Mission Children's
Society
Honolulu, Hawaii

Henry Francis du Pont Winterthur Museum
Winterthur, Delaware

Heritage Society of Waco
Waco, Texas

Historic Mobile Preservation
Society
Mobile, Alabama

Historical Museum of Arizona
Prescott, Arizona

Historical Museum of Wabash
Valley
Terre Haute, Indiana

Historical Society of York County
York, Pennsylvania

History Center of St. Lawrence
County
Canton, New York

Holland Land Office Museum
Batavia, New York

Hood River County Historical
Museum
Hood River, Oregon

House of Refuge Museum
Stuart, Florida

Howard County Historical Society
Kokomo, Indiana

Imperial County Pioneer Museum
Imperial, California

Jacksonville Museum
Jacksonville, Oregon

James Monroe Law Office and
Museum
Fredericksburg, Virginia

Jefferson County Historical Museum
Port Townsend, Washington

Jefferson Davis Shrine and Museum
Biloxi, Mississippi

John and Mable Ringling Museum
of Art
Sarasota, Florida

John Paul Jones House
Portsmouth, New Hampshire

John Woodman Higgins Armory,
Inc.
Worcester, Massachusetts

Kansas City Museum Association
Kansas City, Missouri

Kenosha County Historical Museum
Kenosha, Wisconsin

Kentucky Museum and Library
Bowling Green, Kentucky

La Casa de Rancho los Cerritos
Long Beach, California

Lake County Historical Society
Tavares, Florida

Lancaster County Historical Society
Lancaster, Pennsylvania

Liberty Memorial
Kansas City, Missouri

Lorain County Historical Society
Museum
Elyria, Ohio

Los Angeles County Museum

27

Los Angeles, California

Lotos Club
New York, New York

Louisiana State Museum
New Orleans, Louisiana

Lovely Lane Museum of the
Baltimore Conference, Methodist
Historical Society
Baltimore, Maryland

Lyman Allyn Museum
New London, Connecticut

Madison Historical Society
Madison, Connecticut

Manchester Historic Association
Manchester, New Hampshire

Marine Historical Association,Inc.
Mystic, Connecticut

Mary Buie Museum
Oxford, Mississippi

Maryland Historical Society
Baltimore, Maryland

Mercer County Historical Society
Mercer, Pennsylvania

Metropolitan Museum of Art
New York, New York

M. H. De Young Memorial
Museum
San Francisco, California

Michigan State University Museum
East Lansing, Michigan

Middlebury Historical Society
Wyoming, New York

Milwaukee Public Museum
Milwaukee, Wisconsin

Minnesota Historical Society
Museum
St. Paul, Minnesota

Missouri Historical Society
St. Louis, Missouri

Montclair Art Museum
Montclair, New Jersey

Montgomery Museum of Fine Arts
Montgomery, Alabama

Morristown National Historical
Park
Morristown, New Jersey

Murray County Historical Society
Slayton, Minnesota

Museum for the Arts of Decoration
New York, New York

Museum, National Society, D. A. R.
Washington, D. C.

Museun of Anthropology
Sante Fe, New Mexico

Museum of Art
Albany, New York

Museum of Art, Rhode Island
School of Design
Providence, Rhode Island

Museum of Fine Arts
Boston, Massachusetts

Museum of Historic Costumes,
Texas Women's University
Denton, Texas

Museum of History and Industry
Seattle, Washington

Museum of International Folk Art
Sante Fe, New Mexico

Museum of Motoring Memories
Natural Bridge, Virginia

Museum of Navajo Ceremonial Art
Sante Fe, New Mexico

Museum of New Mexico
Sante Fe, New Mexico

28

Museum of New Mexico State
University
University Park, New Mexico

Museum of Northern Arizona
Flagstaff, Arizona

Museum of the American Indian
New York, New York

Museum of the City of New York
New York, New York

Museum of the Fur Trade
Chadron, Nebraska

Museum of the Plains Indian
Browning, Montana

Nassau County Historical Museum
East Meadow, Long Island,
New York

National Air Museum
Washington, D. C.

National Baseball Hall of Fame
and Museum, Inc.
Cooperstown, New York

Nebraska State Historical Society
Lincoln, Nebraska

Nevada Historical Society
Reno, Nevada

Nevada State Museum
Carson City, Nevada

Neville Public Museum
Green Bay, Wisconsin

New Hampshire Historical Society
Concord, New Hampshire

New Hanover County Museum
Wilmington, North Carolina

New Haven Colony Historical
Society
New Haven, Connecticut

New Jersey Historical Society

Museum
Newark, New Jersey

New Mexico State University
Museum
University Park, New Mexico

New Milford Historical Society
New Milford, Connecticut

New York State Education Building Museum
Albany, New York

Newport Historical Society
Newport, Rhode Island

Nordica Homestead
Farmington, Maine

Norfolk Museum of Arts and
Sciences
Norfolk, Virginia

North Dakota Institute
Fargo, North Dakota

Northampton County Historical
and Genealogical Society
Easton, Pennsylvania

Northampton Historical Society
Museum
Northampton, Massachusetts

Northern Indiana Historical
Society
South Bend, Indiana

Norwegian-American Historical
Museum
Luther College, Decorah, Iowa

Nutley Historical Society Museum
Nutley, New Jersey

Oakland Public Museum
Oakland, California

Oberlin College Art Museum
Oberlin, Ohio

Oconto County Historical Museum

Oconto, Wisconsin

Ohio State Museum
Columbus, Ohio

Old Court House Museum
Vicksburg, Mississippi

Old Fort Historical Museum
Fort Scott, Kansas

Old Sturbridge Village
Sturbridge, Massachusetts

Olmsted County Historical Society
Rochester, Minnesota

Oregon Historical Society
Portland, Oregon

Ossining Historical Society Museum
Ossining, New York

Oysterponds Historical Society,Inc.
Orient, Long Island, New York

Paramus Historical and Preservation Society
Ridgewood, New Jersey

Pasadena Art Museum
Pasadena, California

Pejepscot Historical Society
Brunswick, Maine

Pennsylvania Farm Museum of Landis Valley
Lancaster, Pennsylvania

Pettigrew Museum
Sioux Falls, South Dakota

Philadelphia Museum of Art
Philadelphia, Pennsylvania

Philbrook Art Center
Tulsa, Oklahoma

Pilgrim Hall
Plymouth, Massachusetts

Pioneer Museum and Haggin

Galleries
Stockton, California

Pipe Spring National Monument
Moccasin, Arizona

Plymouth Antiquarian Society
Plymouth, Massachusetts

Ponca City Indian Museum
Ponca City, Oklahoma

Pond Hill Farm
Wallingford, Connecticut

Pope County Historical Society
Glenwood, Minnesota

Porter-Phelps-Huntington Historic House Museum
Hadley, Massachusetts

Portsmouth Historical Society
Portsmouth, Rhode Island

Prescott Historical Society
Prescott, Arizona

Preservation Society of Newport County
Newport, Rhode Island

Quartermaster Museum
Fort Lee, Virginia

Red Cross National Headquarters Museum
Washington, D. C.

Remington Art Memorial
Ogdensburg, New York

Rest Cottage
Evanston, Illinois

Riley County Historical Museum
Manhatten, Kansas

Ringling Circus Museum
Sarasota, Florida

Roanoke River Museum
Boydton, Virginia

30

Robert Hull Fleming Museum
Burlington, Vermont

Rochester Historical Society
Rochester, New York

Rochester Museum of Arts and
Sciences
Rochester, New York

Rocky Ford Museum
Rocky Ford, Colorado

Rosicrucian Art Gallery
San Jose, California

Rush County Historical Society
Rushville, Indiana

St. Petersburg Historical Museum
St. Petersburg, Florida

San Jacinto Monument and Museum
Houston, Texas

Seattle Art Museum
Seattle, Washington

Shaker Colony Museum
Canterbury, New Hampshire

Shaker Historical Society
Shaker Heights, Ohio

Shaker Museum
Old Chatham, New York

Sharlot Hall Museum
Prescott, Arizona

Sheldon Swope Art Gallery
Terre Haute, Indiana

Slater Memorial Museum
Norwich, Connecticut

Sleepy Hollow Restorations
Tarrytown, New York

Smith's Castle
Wickford, Rhode Island

Society for the Preservation of

Historic Landmarks in York
County, Inc.
York, Maine

Society for the Preservation of
New England Antiquities
Boston, Massachusetts

Southwest Museum
Los Angeles, California

Spanish Fort and Museum
Pascagoula, Mississippi

Springfield Historical Society
Springfield, New Jersey

Stanton House
Clinton, Connecticut

State Capitol Historical Museum
Olympia, Washington

State Historical Society of
Wisconsin
Madison, Wisconsin

State Museum
Denver, Colorado

State of Alabama, Department of
Archives and History
Montgomery, Alabama

Staten Island Italian Historical
Society
Staten Island, New York

Swarthmore College, Friends
Historical Library
Swarthmore, Pennsylvania

Tennessee State Museum
Nashville, Tennessee

Texas Memorial Museum
Austin, Texas

Textile Museum
Washington, D. C.

Traphagen School of Fashion,
Museum Collection

New York, New York

Tryon County Muzzle Loaders,
Inc.
Fort Plain, New York

United States Army Infantry
Museum
Fort Benning, Georgia

United States National Museum,
Costume Division
Washington, D. C.

United States Women's Army
Corps Center, Edith Nourse
Rogers Museum
Fort McClellan, Alabama

United States Women's Army
Corps Museum
Washington, D. C.

University Museum, University
of Pennsylvania
Philadelphia, Pennslyvania

University of Arizona Art
Gallery
Tucson, Arizona

University of Rhode Island,
Textile and Clothing Department
Kingston, Rhode Island

University of Washington, Home
Economics Department
Seattle, Washington

Valentine Museum
Richmond, Virginia

Vandalia Historical Society
Museum
Vandalia, Illinois

Virginia City-Madison County
Historical Museum
Virginia City, Montana

Wadsworth Atheneum
Hartford, Connecticut

Walters Art Gallery
Baltimore, Maryland

Warsaw Historical Society
Warsaw, New York

Washington State Museum
Seattle, Washington

Washtenaw Historical Society
Ann Arbor, Michigan

Waterloo Library and Historical
Society
Waterloo, New York

Wenham Historical Association
and Museum, Inc.
Wenham, Massachusetts

Western Reserve Historical
Society
Cleveland, Ohio

West Point Museum
West Point, New York

Whaling Museum
New Bedford, Massachusetts

Whitney Gallery of Western Art
Cody, Wyoming

William Rockhill Nelson Gallery
of Art
Kansas City, Missouri

Wilmette Historical Commission
Wilmette, Illinois

Winnetka Historical Society
Winnetka, Illinois

Witte Memorial Museum
San Antonio, Texas

Worcester Historical Society
Worcester, Massachusetts

York Institute
Saco, Maine

PART I

Institutions

By

Clothing and Clothing Accessory

Canada

United States

Institutions Arranged by Clothing
and Accessories Collected

Master Code

c - Century
A - Casual clothing
B - Formal clothing
C - Children's clothing
E - Ecclesiastical clothing
F - Female clothing
H - Headdress
J - Jewelry
M - Male clothing
N - National clothing
P - Professional clothing
R - Regional clothing
S - Accessories
T - Civil clothing
U - Unclassified clothing as to century
X - Military clothing
Y - Armor
Z - Ceremonial clothing

ACCESSORIES

Accessory Code

c - Century
C - Children
F - Female
M - Male
U - Unclassified as to century

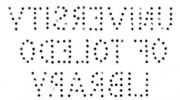

Accessories - Ceremonial
United States - Canada
Kamloops Museum Association,
Kamloops, B. C.   cf. p. 13
U; M
Oakland Public Museum, Oak-
land Calif.   cf. p. 14   18c;
F-M, 19c; F-M, 20c; F-M

Accessories - Ecclesiastical
United States - Canada
Notre Dame Church, Montreal,
Que.   cf. p. 13   17c; M,
18c; M

Accessories - Formal and
Casual
United States - Canada
Beloit Historical Museum,
Beloit, Wisc.   cf. p. 21   19c;
C-F-M
Beverly Historical Society,
Beverly, Mass.   cf. p. 16
19c
Brick Store Museum, Kenne-
bunk, Maine   cf. p. 16   20c;
C-F-M
Charleston Museum, Charleston,
S. C.   cf. p. 21   18c; F-M,
19c; F-M, 20c; F-M
Chicago Historical Society,
Chicago, Ill.   cf. p. 15   19c;
F-M, 20c; F-M
Davenport Public Museum,
Davenport, Iowa   cf. p. 15
19c; F-M 20c; F-M
Detroit Historical Museum,
Detroit, Mich.   cf. p. 17   19c;
F-M, 20c; F-M
Detroit Institute of Arts, Detroit,
Mich.   cf. p. 17   19c; F-M
Dwight-Barnard House, Deer-
field, Mass.   cf. p. 16   18c;
F-M, 19c; F-M, 20c; F-M
Essex Institute, Salem, Mass.

cf. p. 17   18c; F-M, 19c;
F-M
Goyette Museum of Americana,
Peterborough, N. H.   cf. p. 18
U; M
Harrison Gray Otis House, Bos-
ton, Mass.   cf. p. 16   18c;
F-M, 19c; F
Jacksonville Museum, Jackson-
ville, Oreg.   cf. p. 20   19c;
F-M
John Paul Jones House, Ports-
mouth, N. H.   cf. p. 18   19c;
F-M
Kansas City Museum Association,
Kansas City, Mo.   cf. p. 17
18c; C-F-M, 19c; C-F-M, 20c;
C-F-M
La Casa de Rancho Los Cerritos,
Long Beach, Calif.   cf. p. 13
19c; F-M
Marine Historical Association,
Inc., Mystic, Conn.   cf. p. 14
19c; C-F-M, 20c; F
Missouri Historical Society, St.
Louis, Mo.   cf. p. 17   18c;
F-M, 19c; F-M, 20c; F-M
Museum for the Arts of Deco-
ration, New York City, New
York   cf. p. 19   U; F-M
Museum of Fine Arts, Boston,
Mass.   cf. p. 16   16c; C-F-M,
17c; C-F-M, 18c; C-F-M, 19c;
C-F-M, 20c; C-F-M
Museum of the City of New York
New York, N. Y.   cf. p. 19
18c; C-F-M, 19c; C-F-M
Museum, National Society, Daugh-
ters of the American Revolution,
Washington, D. C.   cf. p. 14
18c; C-F-M, 19c; C-F-M
New Hampshire Historical Society,
Concord, N. H.   cf. p. 18   19c;
C-F-M, 20c; C-F-M
Oakland Public Museum, Oakland,

Calif. cf. p.14 18c; F-M,
19c; F-M, 20c; F-M
Pettigrew Museum, Sioux Falls,
S.D. cf. p.21 19c; C-F-M,
20c; C-F-M
Rochester Museum of Arts and
Sciences, Rochester, N.Y.
cf. p.19 19c; F-M, 20c;
F-M
Royal Ontario Museum, Toronto,
Ont. cf. p.13 17c; F-M,
18c; F-M, 19c; F-M, 20c;
F-M
Swarthmore College Friends
Historical Library, Swarth-
more, Penn. cf. p.20
19c; F-M
Traphagen School of Fashion,
New York, N.Y. cf. p.19
12c; F-M, 13c; F-M, 14c;
F-M, 15c; F-M, 16c; F-M,
17c; F-M, 18c; F-M, 19c;
F-M, 20c; F-M, U; F-M
Valentine Museum, Richmond,
Va. cf. p.21 18c; F-M,
19c; F-M
Worcester Historical Society,
Worcester, Mass. cf. p.17
20c; C-F-M

Accessories - Military
United States - Canada
Museum, National Society,
Daughters of the American
Revolution, Washington, D.C.
cf. p.14 18c; M, 19c; M
Royal Canadian Engineers
Museum, Vedder Crossing,
B.C. cf. p.13 18c; M,
19c; M, 20c; M

ARMOR

Armor Code

c - Century
M - Male
U - Unclassified as to century

Armour
United States - Canada
Dallas Historical Society, Hall
of State, Dallas, Texas cf.
p. 21 16c; M, 17c; M, 18c;
M, 19c; M
George F. Harding Museum,
Chicago, Ill. cf. p.15 14c;
M
John Woodman Higgins Armory,
Inc., Worcester, Mass. cf.
p.17 16c; M, 17c; M
M. H. De Young Memorial
Museum, San Francisco, Calif.
cf. p.14 U; M
Winnetka Historical Society,
Winnetka, Ill. cf. p.15 19c;
M, 20c; M
Witte Memorial Museum, San
Antonio, Texas cf. p.21 U;
M

CEREMONIAL CLOTHING

Ceremonial Clothing Code

c - Century
C - Children
F - Female
M - Male
U - Unclassified as to century

Ceremonial Clothing
United States - Canada
Allen County-Fort Wayne Histori-
cal Museum, Fort Wayne, Ind.
cf. p.15 19c; F
Ashland, Lexington, Ky. cf. p.16
19c; F-M
Beloit Historical Museum, Beloit,
Wisc. cf. p.21 19c; C
Beverly Historical Society, Beverly,
Mass. cf. p.16 19c; F
Beyer Home, Oconto County His-
torical Museum, Oconto, Wisc.
cf. p.22 19c; F-M
Bostonian Society, Boston, Mass.
cf. p.16 18c; F
Boulder Pioneer Museum, Boulder,
Colo. cf. p.14 17c; F, 18c;
F, 19c; F, 20c; F
Brick Store Museum, Kennebunk,
Maine cf. p.16 19c; F-M,

20c; F

Camden County Historical Society, Camden, N.J. cf. p.18 19c; F

Carnegie Museum, Pittsburgh, Penna. cf. p.20 19c; M

Charles W. Bowers Memorial Museum, Santa Ana, Calif. cf. p.14 19c; F

City Art Museum of St. Louis, St. Louis, Mo. cf. p.17 19c; F-M

Cole County Historical Society, Jefferson City, Mo. cf. p.17 U;F

Confederate Museum, Richmond, Va. cf. p.21 19c; M

Dallas Historical Society, Hall of State, Dallas, Tex. cf. p.21 19c; F, 20c; F

Danbury Scott-Fanton Museum and Historical Society, Inc., Danbury, Conn. cf. p.14 19c; C-F

Dwight-Barnard House, Deerfield, Mass. cf. p.16 18c; M

East Hampton Historical Society, East Hampton, L.I., N.Y. cf. p.18 18c; F, 19c. F

E. M. Violette Museum, Kirksville, Mo. cf. p.17 19c; F, 20c; F

First White House of the Confederacy, Montgomery, Ala. cf. p.13 19c; M

Florida State Museum, Gainesville, Fla. cf. p.15 19c; F

Garrett County Historical Society, Oakland, Md. cf. p.16 19c; C

Heritage Society of Waco, Waco, Texas cf. p.21 U; F

Historical Society of York County, York, Penna. cf. p.20 19c; F

Hood River County Historical Museum, Hood River, Oreg. cf. p.20 19c; F

Howard County Historical Society, Kokomo, Ind. cf. p.15 19c; F, 20c; F

Imperial County Pioneer Museum, Imperial, Calif. cf. p.13 19c; F

James Monroe Law Office and Museum, Fredericksburg, Va. cf. p.21 18c; C-F-M, 19c; C-F-M, 20c; C-F-M

Jefferson Davis Shrine and Museum, Biloxi, Miss. cf. p.17 19c; F-M

La Casa de Rancho Los Cerritos, Long Beach, Calif. cf. p.13 19c; F

Lorain County Historical Society, Elyria, Ohio cf. p.20 19c; F, 20c; F

Louisiana State Museum, New Orleans, La. cf. p.16 19c; F

Marine Historical Association, Inc., Mystic, Conn. cf. p.14 19c; F-M

Mercer County Historical Society, Mercer, Penna. cf. p.20 18c; F-M

M.H. De Young Memorial Museum, San Francisco, Calif. cf. p.14 U

Middlebury Historical Society, Wyoming, N.Y. cf. p.19 19c; F

Minnesota Historical Society Museum, St. Paul, Minn. cf. p.17 19c; F

Montclair Art Museum, Montclair, N.J. cf. p.18 18c; F-M

Montgomery Museum of Fine Arts, Montgomery, Ala. cf. p.13 19c; F

Murray County Historical Society, Slayton, Minn. cf. p.17 19c; F-M

Museum of Historic Costumes, Texas Women's University, Denton, Texas cf. p.21 19c; F, 20c; F

Museum of Navajo Ceremonial Art, Santa Fe, N.Mex. cf. p.18 19c; F

Museum of New Mexico, Santa Fe, N. Mex. cf. p.18 19c; F-M

Museum of Northern British Columbia, Prince Rupert, B.C.

cf. p.13 U; F-M

Museum of the American Indian, New York, N.Y. cf. p.19 N; F-M

Museum of the Plains Indian, Browning, Mont. cf. p.17 19c; F-M

Nassau County Historical Museum, East Meadow, L.I., N.Y. cf. p.18 19c; F, 20c; F

New Milford Historical Society, New Milford, Conn. cf. p. 14 18c; F

North Dakota Institute, Fargo, N.D. cf. p.19 19c; F

Northern Indian Historical Society, South Bend, Ind. cf. p.15 19c; F

Norwegian-American Historical Museum, Decorah, Iowa cf. p.16 N; F-M, 18c; F, 19c; F-M

Nutley Historical Society Museum, Nutley, N.J. cf. p. 18 19c; F

Oakland Public Museum, Oakland, Calif. cf. p.14 18c; F-M, 19c; F-M, N; F-M

Old Court House Museum, Vicksburg, Miss. cf. p.17 18c; M

Ossining Historical Society Museum, Ossining, N.Y. cf. p.19 19c; F-M

Paramus Historical and Preservation Society, Ridgewood, N.J. cf. p.18 18c; F, 19c; F

Pettigrew Museum, Sioux Falls, S.D. cf. p.21 19c; F-M, 20c; F-M

Pilgrim Society, Plymouth, Mass. cf. p.17 17c; F

Ponca City Indian Museum, Ponca City, Okla. cf. p.20 19c; F-M

Pope County Historical Society, Glenwood, Minn. cf. p.17 19c; M, 20c; F

Porter-Phelps-Huntington Historical House Museum, Hadley, Mass. cf. p.16 18c; F

Rochester Museum of Arts and Sciences, Rochester, N.Y. cf. p.19 19c; C-F

San Jacinto Monument and Museum, Houston, Texas cf. p.21 19c; F

Seattle Art Museum, Seattle, Wash. cf. p.21 U; F

Sharlot Hall, Historical Museum of Arizona, Prescott, Ariz. cf. p.13 19c; F

Sheldon Swope Art Gallery, Terre Haute, Ind. cf. p.15 19c; F, 20c; F

Spanish Fort Museum, Pascagoula, Miss. cf. p.17 19c; F

Stanton House, Clinton, Conn. cf. p.14 19c; F

Traphagen School of Fashion, Museum Collection, New York, N.Y. cf. p.19 19c; F, 20c; F

Valentine Museum, Richmond, Va. cf. p.21 18c; F, 19c; F

Virginia City-Madison County Historical Museum, Virginia City, Mont. cf. p.17 19c; F

Wilmette Historical Commission, Wilmette, Ill. cf. p.15 19c; F

Witte Memorial Museum, San Antonio, Texas cf. p.21 N; F-M

Worcester Historical Society, Worcester, Mass. cf. p.17 19c; F, 20c; F

CIVIL UNIFORMS

Civil Uniform Code

c - Century
F - Female
M - Male
U - Unclassified as to century

Civil Uniforms
United States - Canada

Beyer Home, Oconto County Historical Museum, Oconto, Wisc. cf. p.22 19c; M

Bostonian Society, Boston, Mass. cf. p.16 19c; M

Charleston Museum, Charleston, S.C. cf. p.21 19c; M

Colonial Williamsburg, Inc.,
Williamsburg, Va. cf. p. 21
18c; F-M
Danbury Scott-Fanton Museum
and Historical Society, Inc.,
Danbury, Conn. cf. p. 14
18c; M
Guilford Courthouse National
Military Park, Greensboro,
N. C. cf. p. 19 19c; M
Manchester Historical Associ-
ation, Manchester, N. H.
cf. p. 18 19c; M
Marine Historical Association,
Inc., Mystic, Conn. cf.
p. 14 U; M
Mercer County Historical So-
ciety, Mercer, Penna. cf.
p. 20 18c; M, 19c; M
San Jacinto Monument and Mu-
seum, Houston, Texas cf.
p. 21 17c; M, 18c; M
Seattle Art Museum, Seattle,
Wash. cf. p. 21 U; M
State Museum, The State His-
torical Society of Colorado,
Denver, Colo. cf. p. 14
19c; C-M, 20c; M

ECCLESIASTICAL VESTMENTS

Ecclesiastical Vestment Code

B - Formal
c - Century
F - Female
M - Male
U - Unclassified as to century

Ecclesiastical Vestments
United States - Canada
Beyer Home, Oconto County
Historical Museum, Oconto,
Wisc. cf. p. 22 20c; B-M
Charles W. Bowers Memorial
Museum, Santa Ana, Calif.
cf. p. 14 19c; B-M
Cincinnati Art Museum, Cincin-
nati, Ohio cf. p. 19 N; B-M
City Art Museum of St. Louis,
St. Louis, Mo. cf. p. 17
17c; B-M, 18c; B-M, 19c;
B-M

Concordia Historical Institute,
St. Louis, Mo. cf. p. 17
18c; B-M, 19c; B-M
Costume Center, Museum of Art,
Providence, R. I. cf. p. 20
N; B-M
Dallas Historical Society, Hall of
State, Dallas, Texas cf. p. 21
18c; B-M, 19c; B-M, 20c; B-M
Delaware State Museum, Dover,
Del. cf. p. 14 18c; B-M
Detroit Institute of Arts, Detroit,
Mich. cf. p. 17 19c; B-M
Dwight-Barnard House, Deerfield,
Mass. cf. p. 16 18c; B-M,
19c; B-M, 20c; B-M
Erie Public Museum, Erie, Penna.
cf. p. 20 18c; B-M, 19c; B-M
Fogg Art Museum, Cambridge,
Mass. cf. p. 16 16c; B-M,
17c; B-M, 18c; B-M, 19c; B-M
Hall of History, Raleigh, N. C.
cf. p. 19 18c; B-M, 19c; B-M,
20c; B-M
Los Angeles County Museum, Los
Angeles, Calif. cf. p. 14 15c;
B-M, 16c; B-M, 18c; B-M,
20c; B-M
M. H. De Young Memorial Museum,
San Francisco, Calif. cf.
p. 14 17c; B-M, 18c; B-M
Minnesota Historical Society Mu-
seum, St. Paul, Minn. cf.
p. 17 19c; B-M
Museum of Fine Arts, Boston,
Mass. cf. p. 16 16c; B-M,
17c; B-M, 19c; B-M, 20c; B-M
Museum of New Mexico, Santa Fe,
N. Mex. cf. p. 18 19c; B-M,
N; B-M
Museum of the American Indian,
New York, N. Y. cf. p. 19
18c; B-M, 19c; B-M, 20c; B-M
Museum of the Fur Trade, Chad-
ron, Nebr. cf. p. 17 19c; B-M
Norfolk Museum of Arts and
Sciences, Norfolk, Va. cf. p.
21 19c; B-M, 20c; B-M
North Dakota Institute, Fargo, N.D.
cf. p. 19 19c; B-M
Norwegian-American Historical
Museum, Decorah, Iowa cf.
p. 16 18c; B-M, 19c; B-M

Notre Dame Church, Montreal,
Que. cf. p. 13 17c; M, 18c;
M, 20c; M
Pettigrew Museum, Sioux Falls,
S.D. cf. p. 21 19c; F-M,
20c; F-M
Philadelphia Museum of Art,
Philadelphia, Penna. cf. p.
20 18c; B-M, 19c; B-M,
20c; B-M
Royal Ontario Museum, Toronto,
Ont. cf. p. 13 17c; M, 18c;
M, 19c; M, 20c; M
San Jacinto Monument and Mu-
seum, Houston, Texas cf.
p. 21 18c; B-M
Wadsworth Atheneum, Hartford,
Conn. cf. p. 14 18c; B-M,
19c; B-M, 20c; B-M
Walters Art Gallery, Baltimore,
Md. cf. p. 16 15c; B-M,
16c; B-M, 17c; B-M, 18c;
B-M
York Institute, Saco, Maine
cf. p. 16 18c; B-M

Ecclesiastical Lay Clothing
United States - Canada
Essex Institute, Salem, Mass.
cf. p. 17 N; A-B-F-M
M.H. De Young Memorial Mu-
seum, San Francisco, Calif.
cf. p. 14 19c; A-F
Nassau County Historical Mu-
seum, East Meadow, L. I.,
N.Y. cf. p. 18 19c; B-F,
20c; B-F
Pennsylvania Farm Museum of
Landis Valley, Lancaster,
Penna. cf. p. 20 19c; A-B-
C-F-M, 20c; A-B-C-F-M
Pilgrim Society, Plymouth,
Mass. cf. p. 17 17c; A-B-
C-F
Rochester Museum of Arts and
Sciences, Rochester, N.Y.
cf. p. 19 17c; A-B-F-M
Traphagen School of Fashion,
Museum Collection, New York,
N.Y. cf. p. 19 N; A-B-
F-M
Worcester Historical Society,
Worcester, Mass. cf. p. 17

18c; A-B-C-F-M

FORMAL AND CASUAL
CLOTHING

Formal and Casual Clothing Code

c - Century
A - Casual clothing
B - Formal clothing
C - Children's clothing
F - Female clothing
M - Male
U - Unclassified as to century

Formal and Casual Clothing
United States - Canada
Alamo, San Antonio, Texas cf.
p. 21 19c; A-M
Aldrich Collection, Providence,
R.I. cf. p. 20 N; A-B-F-M
Allen County-Fort Wayne His-
torical Museum, Fort Wayne,
Ind. cf. p. 15 19c; B-F
Allen County Museum, Lima,
Ohio cf. p. 20 19c; A-B-F-M
American Museum of Comedy,
Crestwood, N.Y. cf. p. 18
20c; B-F-M
Anoka County Historical Society,
Anoka, Minn. cf. p. 17 19c;
A-B-F, 20c; A-B-F
Arizona Pioneers' Historical
Society, Tucson, Ariz. cf.
p. 13 N; A-B-F-M
Arizona State Museum, Tucson,
Ariz. cf. p. 13 19c; A-B-F-
M, 20c; A-B-F-M
Ashland, Lexington, Ky. cf.
p. 16 19c; A-B-F-M
Aurora Historical Society, Inc.,
Aurora, Ill. cf. p. 15 19c;
A-F, 20c; A-F
Baltimore Museum of Art, Balti-
more, Md. cf. p. 16 N; A-B-
F-M
Beloit Historical Museum, Beloit,
Wisc. cf. p. 21 19c; A-B-C-
D-F-M
Bennington Historical Museum,
Bennington, Vt. cf. p. 21 18c;
A-B-F-M, 19c; A-B-F-M, 20c;
A-B-F-M

40

Beverly Historical Society,
Beverly, Mass. cf. p.16
19c; A-B-C-F-M
Beyer Home, Oconto County
Historical Museum, Oconto,
Wisc. cf. p.22 19c; A-B-
C-F-M
Bostonian Society, Boston, Mass.
cf. p.16 18c; A-B-C-F-M,
19c; B-M
Boulder Pioneer Museum,
Boulder, Colo. cf. p.14
17c; B-F, 18c; B-F, 19c;
A-B-F-M, 20c; B-F-M
Brick Store Museum, Kennebunk,
Maine cf. p.16 19c; A-B-
F-M, 20c; B-C-D-F-M
Brooklyn Museum, Brooklyn,
N.Y. cf. p.18 18c; A-B-
F-M, 19c; A-B-F-M, 20c;
A-B-F-M
Buffalo Bill Historical Center,
Buffalo Bill Museum, Cody,
Wyo. cf. p.22 19c; A-B-
F-M
Buffalo Museum of Science,
Buffalo, N.Y. cf. p.18
19c; A-B-F-M, 20c; A-B-
F-M
Camden County Historical So-
ciety, Camden, N.J. cf.
p.18 19c; A-B-F
Campbell House Museum, St.
Louis, Mo. cf. p.17 19c;
A-B-F, 20c; A-B-C-F
Campus Martius Museum,
Marietta, Ohio cf. p.20
18c; A-B-F-M, 19c; A-B-
F-M
Carnegie Museum, Pittsburgh,
Penna. cf. p.20 19c; A-B-
C-D-F-M, 20c; A-B-F-M
Charleston Museum, Charleston,
S.C. cf. p.21 18c; A-B-
D-F-M, 19c; A-B-D-F-M,
20c; A-B-D-F-M
Charles W. Bowers Memorial
Museum, Santa Ana, Calif.
cf. p.14 19c; A-B-D-F-M
Chicago Historical Society,
Chicago, Ill. cf. p.15 19c;
A-B-D-F-M, 20c; A-B-D-F-M
Cincinnati Art Museum, Cin-

cinnati, Ohio cf. p.19 16c;
A-B-C-F-M, 17c; A-B-C-F-M,
18c; A-B-C-F-M, 19c; A-B-C-
F-M, 20c; A-B-C-F-M, U; A-
B-F-M, N; A-B-D-F-M
City Art Museum of St. Louis,
St. Louis, Mo. cf. p.17 19c;
A-B-C-F-M
Clay County Historical Society,
Moorhead, Minn. cf. p.17
19c; A-B-F-M
Cleveland Public Library, Cleve-
land, Ohio cf. p.19 U; A-B-
F-M
Colebrook Historical Society,
Colebrook, Conn. cf. p.14
19c; A-B-C-F-M, 20c; A-B-
F-M
Colonial Williamsburg Inc.,
Williamsburg, Va. cf. p.21
18c; A-B-F-M
Concordia Historical Institute,
St. Louis, Mo. cf. p.17
18c; A-B-F-M, 19c; A-B-F-M
Confederate Museum, Richmond,
Va. cf. p.21 19c; B-M
Connecticut Historical Society,
Hartford, Conn. cf. p.14
18c; A-B-F-M, 19c; A-B-F-M
Costume Center, Museum of Art,
Providence, R.I. cf. p.20
N; A-B-F-M
Dallas Historical Society, Dallas,
Texas cf. p.21 18c; A-B-F-
M, 19c; A-B-C-D-F-M, 20c;
A-B-C-F-M
Danbury Scott-Fanton Museum and
Historical Society, Inc., Dan-
bury, Conn. cf. p.14 19c;
A-B-C-F-M
Davenport Public Museum, Daven-
port, Iowa cf. p.15 19c; A-
B-D-F-M, 20c; A-B-D-F-M
Delaware State Museum, Dover,
Del. cf. p.14 18c; A-B-F-M,
19c; A-B-F-M
Detroit Historical Museum, Detroit,
Mich. cf. p.17 19c; A-B-D-F-
M, 20c; A-B-D-F-M
Detroit Institute of Arts, Detroit,
Mich. cf. p.17 18c; A-B-F-
M, 19c; A-D-F
DeWitt Historical Society of

Tompkins County, Inc.,
Ithaca, N. Y. cf. p. 19 19c;
A-B-F-M
Dundurn Castle Museum, Ham-
ilton, Ont. cf. p. 13 U;
A-B-F-M
East Hampton Historical So-
ciety, East Hampton, L. I.,
N. Y. cf. p. 18 18c; A-B-
F, 19c; A-B-F
E. M. Violette Museum, Kirks-
ville, Mo. cf. p. 17
600 B. C.; A-B-F-M, 19c;
A-B-C-D-F-M, 20c; A-B-C-
D-F-M
Erie Public Museum, Erie,
Penna. cf. p. 20 18c; A-
B-F-M, 19c; A-B-F-M
Essex Institute, Salem, Mass.
cf. p. 17 17c; A-B-F-M,
18c; A-B-D-F-M, 19c; A-B-
D-F-M
Farmers' Museum, Coopers-
town, N. Y. cf. p. 18 19c;
A-B-F-M
First White House of the Con-
federacy, Montgomery, Ala.
cf. p. 13 19c; A-M
Florida State Museum, Gaines-
ville, Fla. cf. p. 15 19c;
B-F
Garrett County Historical So-
ciety, Oakland, Md. cf.
p. 16 19c; B-C
Goyette Museum of Americana,
Peterborough, N. H. cf. p.
18 U; A-B-D-F-M
Greensboro Historical Museum,
Greensboro, N. C. cf. p. 19
19c; A-B-F-M, 20c; A-B-
F-M
Hall of History, Raleigh, N. C.
cf. p. 19 18c; A-B-F-M,
19c; A-B-C-F-M, 20c; A-B-
C-F-M
Harrison Gray Otis House,
Boston, Mass. cf. p. 16
18c; A-B-D-F-M, 19c; A-B-
D-F
Harvard College Library, Cam-
bridge, Mass. cf. p. 16
19c; B-F-M, 20c; B-F-M
Henry Francis du Pont Winter-

thur Museum, Winterthur, Del.
cf. p. 14 18c; A-B-F-M, 19c;
A-C-F
Heritage Society of Waco, Waco,
Texas cf. p. 21 U; B-F
Historic Mobile Preservation So-
ciety, Mobile, Ala. cf. p. 13
19c; A-F
Historical Museum of Wabash
Valley, Terre Haute, Ind. cf.
p. 15 19c; A-B-F-M, 20c; A-
B-F-M
Historical Society of York County,
York, Penna. cf. p. 20 18c;
A-B-M, 19c; A-B-F-M
Holland Land Office Museum,
Batavia, N. Y. cf. p. 18 17c;
B-M, 18c; A-B-F-M
Hood River County Historical Mu-
seum, Hood River, Oreg. cf.
p. 20 19c; B-F, 20c; A-F
House of Refuge Museum, Stuart,
Fla. cf. p. 15 19c; A-B-C-F-
M
Howard County Historical Society,
Kokomo, Ind. cf. p. 15 19c;
B-C-F, 20c; A-B-F
Imperial County Pioneer Museum,
Imperial, Calif. cf. p. 13 19c;
A-B-C-F, 20c; A-B-C-F
Jacksonville Museum, Jackson-
ville, Oreg. cf. p. 20 19c; A-
B-C-D-F-M
James Monroe Law Office and Mu-
seum, Fredericksburg, Va. cf.
p. 21 18c; A-B-F-M, 19c; A-B-
F-M, 20c; A-B-F-M
Jefferson County Historical Museum,
Port Townsend, Wash. cf. p.
21 19c; A-B-F-M, 20c; A-B-
F-M
Jefferson Davis Shrine and Museum,
Biloxi, Miss. cf. p. 17 19c;
A-B-F-M, 20c; A-B-F
John and Mable Ringling Museum
of Art, Sarasota, Fla. cf. p.
15 18c; A-B-F-M
John Paul Jones House, Ports-
mouth, N. H. cf. p. 18 18c;
A-B-F, 19c; A-B-D-F
Kamloops Museum Association,
Kamloops, B. C. cf. p. 13
19c; A-B-F-M, 20c; A-B-F-M,

42

U; A-F-M
Kansas City Museum Association, Kansas City, Mo.
cf. p. 17 18c; A-B-C-D-F-M, 19c; A-B-C-D-F-M, N; A-B-F-M, 20c; A-B-D-C-D-F-M
Kenosha County Historical Museum, Kenosha, Wisc. cf. p. 21 19c; A-B-F-M, 20c; A-F
Kentucky Museum and Library, Bowling Green, Ky. cf. p. 16 U; A-B-F-M
La Casa de Rancho Los Cerritos, Long Beach, Calif. cf. p. 13 19c; A-B-D-F
Lake County Historical Society, Tavares, Fla. cf. p. 15 19c; B-F, 20c; B-F
Lancaster County Historical Society, Lancaster, Penna. cf. p. 20 19c; A-B-F-M
Lennox and Addington County Museum, Napanee, Ont. cf. p. 13 19c; A-B-F-M
Lorain County Historical Society Museum, Elyria Ohio cf. p. 20 19c; A-B-C-F, 20c; A-B-C-F
Los Angeles County Museum, Los Angeles, Calif. cf. p. 14 16c; B-M, 18c; A-B-F-M, 19c; A-B-F-M, 20c; A-B-F-M
Louisiana State Museum, New Orleans, La. cf. p. 16 19c; A-B-F-M, 20c; A-B-F-M
Lovely Land Museum of the Baltimore Conference Methodist Historical Society, Baltimore, Md. cf. p. 16 U; A-B-F-M
Lyman Allyn Museum, New London, Conn. cf. p. 14 18c; A-B-F, 19c; A-B-F, 20c; A-B-F, U; A-B-F-M
Madison Historical Society, Madison, Conn. cf. p. 14 U; A-B-F-M
Manchester Historic Association, Manchester, N. H. cf. p. 18 19c; B-F

Marine Historical Association, Inc., Mystic, Conn. cf. p. 14 19c; A-B-C-D-F-M, N; A-B-D-F-M, 20c; A-B-C-F-M
Mary Buie Museum, Oxford, Miss. cf. p. 17 U; A-B-F-M
Maryland Historical Society, Baltimore, Md. cf. p. 16 18c; A-B-C-F-M, 19c; A-B-C-F-M
Mercer County Historical Society, Mercer, Penna. cf. p. 20 18c; A-B-F-M
M. H. De Young Memorial Museum, San Francisco, Calif. cf. p. 14 19c; A-B-F-M, 20c; B-F
Michigan State University Museum, East Lansing, Mich. cf. p. 17 19c; A-B-F-M, 20c; A-B-F-M
Middlebury Historical Society, Wyoming, N. Y. cf. p. 19 19c; A-B-F
Minnesota Historical Society Museum, St. Paul, Minn. cf. p. 17 19c; A-B-C-F-M, 20c; A-F-M
Missouri Historical Society, St. Louis, Mo. cf. p. 17 18c; A-B-D-F-M, 19c; A-B-D-F-M, 20c; A-B-D-F-M
Montclair Art Museum, Montclair, N. J. cf. p. 18 18c; A-B-C-F-M, 19c; A-B-C-F-M, 20c; A-B-C-F-M, N; A-B-F-M
Montgomery Museum of Fine Arts, Montgomery Ala. cf. p. 13 19c; A-B-F
Morristown National Historical Park, Morristown, N. J. cf. p. 18 18c; A-B-F-M
Murray County Historical Society, Slayton, Minn. cf. p. 17 19c; B-F-M, 20c; A-B-F
Musée de la Province, Quebec, Que. cf. p. 13 19c; A-B-F-M
Museum for the Arts of Decoration, New York, N. Y. cf. p. 19 U; D-F-M
Museum of Art, Albany, N. Y. cf. p. 18 N; A-B-F-M
Museum of Fine Arts, Boston, Mass. cf. p. 16 16c; A-B-C-F-M, 17c; A-B-C-D-F-M, 18c; A-B-C-D-F-M, 19c; A-B-C-D-

F-M, 20c; A-B-C-D-F-M

Museum of History and Industry, Seattle, Wash. cf. p. 21 19c; A-B-C-F-M, 20c; A-B-C-F-M

Museum of Motoring Memories, Natural Bridge, Va. cf. p. 21 20c; A-B-F-M

Museum of Natural History, New York, N.Y. cf. p. 19 19c; A-B-F-M

Museum of Navajo Ceremonial Art, Santa Fe, N. Mex. cf. p. 18 19c; A-F, 20c; A-F

Museum of New Mexico, Santa Fe, N. Mex. cf. p. 18 N; A-B-F-M, 19c; A-B-F-M, 20c; A-B-F-M

Museum of New Mexico State University, University Park, N. Mex. cf. p. 18 U; A-B-F-M

Museum of Northern Arizona, Flagstaff, Ariz. cf. p. 13 19c; A-B-F-M, 20c; A-B-F-M

Museum of Northern British Columbia, Prince Rupert, B.C. cf. p. 13 U; A-B-F-M

Museum of the American Indian, New York, N.Y. cf. p. 19 N; A-B-C-D-F-M, 18c; A-B-F-M, 19c; A-B-F-M, 20c; A-B-F-M

Museum of the City of New York, New York, N.Y. cf. p. 19 17c; A-B-C-F-M, 18c; A-B-C-D-F-M, 19c; A-B-C-F-M, U; A-B-C-F-M

Museum of the Fur Trade, Chadron, Nebr. cf. p. 17 19c; A-B-D-F-M

Museum, National Society, Daughters of the American Revolution, Washington, D.C. cf. p. 14 18c; A-B-C-D-F-M, 19c; A-B-C-D-F-M

Museum of the Plains Indian, Browning, Mont. cf. p. 17 19c; A-F-M

Museum of the Staten Island Italian Historical Society, Staten Island, N.Y. cf. p. 19 U; A-B-F-M

Nassau County Historical Museum, East Meadow, L.I., N.Y. cf. p. 18 19c; A-B-C-F-M, 20c; A-B-C-F-M

Nebraska State Historical Society, Lincoln Nebr. cf. p. 18 19c; B-F-M, 20c; A-F-M

Nevada Historical Society, Reno, Nev. cf. p. 18 19c; A-B-F-M, 20c; A-B-F-M

Nevada State Museum, Carson City, Nev. cf. p. 18 19c; B-F

New Hampshire Historical Society, Concord, N.H. cf. p. 18 19c; A-B-C-D-F-M, 20c; A-B-C-D-F-M

New Haven Colony Historical Society, New Haven, Conn. cf. p. 14 19c; A-B-F-M

New Jersey Historical Society Museum, Newark, N.J. cf. p. 18 19c; A-B-F-M

New Milford Historical Society, New Milford, Conn. cf. p. 14 18c; A-B-C-F-M, 19c; A-B-C-F-M

Newport Historical Society, Newport, R.I. cf. p. 20 18c; A-B-F-M, 19c; A-B-F-M

Niagara Falls Museum, Ltd., Niagara Falls, Ont. cf. p. 13 U; A-B-F-M

Nordica Homestead, Farmington, Maine cf. p. 16 19c; A-B-F

Norfolk Museum of Arts and Sciences, Norfolk, Va. cf. p. 21 19c; A-B-C-F-M, 20c; A-B-C-F-M

Northampton County Historical and Genealogical Society, Easton, Penna. cf. p. 20 U; A-B-F-M

Northampton Historical Society Museum, Northampton, Mass. cf. p. 16 18c; A-B-F-M, 19c; A-B-F-M, 20c; A-B-F-M

North Dakota Institute, Fargo, N.D. cf. p. 19 19c; A-B-F-M, 20c; A-B-F-M

Northern Indiana Historical Society, South Bend, Ind. cf. p. 15 19c; B-F

Norwegian-American Historical Museum, Decorah, Iowa cf. p. 16 N; A-B-F-M, 18c; A-B-C-F-M, 19c; A-B-F-M

Nutley Historical Society Museum, Nutley, N. J. cf. p. 18 19c; A-B-F-M

Oakland Public Museum, Oakland, Calif. cf. p. 14 18c; A-B-D-F-M, 19c; A-B-D-F-M, 20c; A-B-D-F-M, N; A-B-D-F-M

Ohio State Museum, Columbus, Ohio cf. p. 20 19c; B-F-M

Old Court House Museum, Vicksburg, Miss. cf. p. 17 18c; A-M, 19c; A-B-F, 20c; A-B-F

Old Fort Historical Museum, Fort Scott, Kans. cf. p. 16 19c; A-B-F

Old Sturbridge Village, Sturbridge, Mass. cf. p. 17 18c; A-B-F-M, 19c; A-B-F-M

Olmsted County Historical Society, Rochester, Minn. cf. p. 17 19c; A-B-F, 20c; A-B-F

Oregon Historical Society, Portland, Oreg. cf. p. 20 U; A-B-F-M

Ossining Historical Society Museum, Ossining, N. Y. cf. p. 19 18c; B-F, 19c; A-B-D-F, 20c; A-B-F

Oysterponds Historical Society, Inc. , Orient, L. I. , N. Y. cf. p. 19 19c; A-B-C-D-F-M

Paramus Historical and Preservation Society, Ridgewood, N. J. cf. p. 18 18c; B-F, 19c; A-B-F-M, 20c; A-C

Pasadena Art Museum, Pasadena, Calif. cf. p. 14 19c; A-B-F-M

Pejepscot Historical Society, Brunswick, Maine cf. p. 16 19c; A-B-F-M

Pennsylvania Farm Museum of Landis Valley, Lancaster, Penna. cf. p. 20 19c;

A-B-C-F-M, 20c; A-B-C-F-M

Pettigrew Museum, Sioux Falls, S. D. cf. p. 21 19c; A-B-C-D-F-M, 20c; A-B-C-D-F-M

Philadelphia Museum of Art, Philadelphia, Penna. cf. p. 20 18c; A-B-C-F-M, 19c; A-B-C-F-M, 20c; A-B-C-F-M

Philbrook Art Center, Tulsa, Okla. cf. p. 20 U; A-B-F-M

Pilgrim Society, Plymouth, Mass. cf. p. 17 17c; A-B-C-F

Pioneer Museum and Haggin Art Galleries, Stockton, Calif. cf. p. 14 U; A-B-F-M

Pipe Spring National Monument, Moccasin, Ariz. cf. p. 13 19c; A-B-F-M

Plymouth Antiquarian Society, Plymouth, Mass. cf. p. 17 18c; A-B-F-M, 19c; A-B-F-M

Ponca City Indian Museum, Ponca City, Okla. cf. p. 20 19c; B-F-M, 20c; A-C-F

Pond Hill Farm, Wallingford, Conn. cf. p. 14 19c; B-F-M

Pope County Historical Society, Glenwood, Minn. cf. p. 17 19c; B-M, 20c; A-B-D-F-M

Porter-Phelps-Huntington Historic House Museum, Hadley, Mass. cf. p. 16 18c; A-B-F-M, 19c; A-B-F-M

Portsmouth Historical Society, Portsmouth, R. I. cf. p. 20 U; A-B-C-D-F-M

Rest Cottage, Evanston, Ill. cf. p. 15 U; A-B-F-M

Ringling Circus Museum, Sarasota, Fla. cf. p. 15 19c; A-B-F-M, 20c; A-B-F-M

Rochester Historical Society, Rochester, N. Y. cf. p. 19 19c; A-B-F, 20c; A-B-F

Rochester Museum of Arts and Sciences, Rochester, N. Y. cf. p. 19 17c; A-B-F-M, 18c; A-B-M, 19c; A-B-C-D-F-M, 20c; A-B-F-M

Rocky Ford Museum, Rocky Ford, Colo. cf. p. 14 19c; A-B-F-M

Royal Ontario Museum, Toronto, Ont. cf. p. 13 3c; 4c; 5c; 6c;

7c; 17c; 18c; 19c; 20c; U;
A-B-F-M

San Jacinto Monument and Museum, Houston, Texas cf.
p. 21 17c; A-M, 18c; A-M,
19c; A-B-D-F

Seattle Art Museum, Seattle,
Wash. cf. p. 21 U; A-B-
F-M

Shaker Museum, Old Chatham,
N. Y. cf. p. 19 19c; A-B-
F-M, U; A-B-F-M

Sharlot Hall Museum, Prescott,
Ariz. cf. p. 13 19c; A-
B-F

Sheldon Swope Art Gallery,
Terre Haute, Ind. cf. p.
15 16c; B-F, 19c; A-B-
F, 20c; A-B-F

Sleepy Hollow Restorations,
Tarrytown, N. Y. cf. p.
19 18c; A-D-F, 20c;
A-B-F-M

Smithsonian Institution, Washington, D. C. cf. p. 14
18c; A-B-F-M, 19c; A-B-
F-M, 20c; A-B-F-M

Society for the Preservation
of Historic Landmarks in
York County, Inc., York,
Maine cf. p. 16 U; A-B-
F-M

Southwest Museum, Los Angeles,
Calif. cf. p. 14 N; A-B-
F-M

Spanish Fort Museum, Pascagoula, Miss. cf. p. 17
18c; A-B-F-M, 19c; A-B-F

Stanton House, Clinton, Conn.
cf. p. 14 19c; A-B-F

State Capitol Historical Museum, Olympia, Wash. cf.
p. 21 19c; A-F, 20c; A-F-M

State Museum, The State Historical Society of Colorado,
Denver, Colo. cf. p. 14
19c; A-B-C-D-F-M, 20c;
A-B-C-D-F-M

Swarthmore College Friends
Historical Library, Swarthmore, Penna. cf. p. 20
19c; A-B-D-F-M

Tennessee State Museum,

Nashville, Tenn. cf. p. 21
19c; A-B-F

Texas Memorial Museum, Austin,
Texas cf. p. 21 19c; A-B-F-
M, 20c; A-M, N; A-B-F-M

Textile Museum, Washington, D. C.
cf. p. 15 N; A-B-F-M

Traphagen School of Fashion, Museum Collection, New York,
N. Y. cf. p. 19 12c; A-B-D-F-
M, 13c; A-B-D-F-M, 14c; A-
B-D-F-M, 15c; A-B-D-F-M,
16c; A-B-D-F-M, 17c; A-B-D-
F-M, 18c; A-B-D-F-M, 19c;
A-B-D-F-M, 20c; A-B-D-F-M,
N; A-B-F-M, U; A-B-D-F-M

Tryon County Muzzle Loaders,
Inc., Fort Plain, N. Y. cf.
p. 19 18c; A-F-M, 19c; A-F-M

University of Arizona Art Gallery,
Tucson, Ariz. cf. p. 13 U;
A-B-F-M

University of Rhode Island, Costume and Clothing Collection,
Kingston, R. I. cf. p. 20 18c;
A-C-M, 19c; A-B-F-M, 20c;
A-B-F

Valentine Museum, Richmond, Va.
cf. p. 21 17c; A-B-C, 18c;
A-B-C-D-F-M, 19c; A-B-C-D-
F-M, 20c; A-B-F-M

Virginia City-Madison County Historical Museum, Virginia City,
Mont. cf. p. 17 19c; A-B-F-
M, 20c; A-B-F-M

Wadsworth Atheneum, Hartford,
Conn. cf. p. 14 18c; A-B-F-
M, 19c; A-B-C-F-M, 20c; A-
B-C-F-M

Walters Art Gallery, Baltimore,
Md. cf. p. 16 15c; A-B-F-M,
16c; A-B-F-M, 17c; A-B-F-M,
18c; A-B-F-M

Waterloo Historical Society Museum, Kitchener, Ont. cf.
p. 13 U; A-B-F-M

Waterloo Library and Historical
Society, Waterloo, N. Y. cf.
p. 19 19c; A-B-F-M

Western Reserve Historical Society, Cleveland, Ohio cf. p. 19
19c; A-B-F-M, 20c; A-B-F-M

Whaling Museum, New Bedford,

46

Mass. cf. p. 16 19c; A-B-F-M

William Rockhill Nelson Gallery of Art, Kansas City, Mo. cf. p. 17 17c; A-B-F-M, 18c; A-B-F-M, N; A-B-F-M

Wilmette Historical Commission, Wilmette, Ill. cf. p. 15 19c; A-B-F

Winnetka Historical Society, Winnetka, Ill. cf. p. 15 19c; A-B-C-F-M, 20c; A-B-C-F-M

Witte Memorial Museum, San Antonio, Texas cf. p. 21 N; A-B-F-M, 15c; A-B-F-M, 18c; A-B-C-F-M, 19c; A-B-C-F-M

Worcester Historical Society, Worcester, Mass. cf. p. 17 18c; A-B-F-M, 19c; A-B-C-D-F-M, 20c; A-B-C-D-F-M

York Institute, Saco, Maine cf. p. 16 18c; A-B-C-F-M

HEADDRESSES

Headdress Code

c - Century
C - Children
F - Female
M - Male
U - Unclassified as to century

Headdress: Armor
United States - Canada

Beyer Home, Oconto County Historical Museum, Oconto, Wisc. cf. p. 22 20c; M

Dallas Historical Society, Dallas, Texas cf. p. 21 19c; M

George F. Harding Museum, Chicago, Ill. cf. p. 15 14c; M

Marine Historical Association, Inc., Mystic, Conn. cf. p. 14 U; M

M. H. De Young Memorial Museum, San Francisco, Calif.

cf. p. 14 19c; M

Headdress: Ceremonial
United States - Canada

Arizona State Museum, Tucson, Ariz. cf. p. 13 19c; F-M, 20c; F-M, N; F-M

Boulder Pioneer Museum, Boulder, Colo. cf. p. 14 20c; F

Buffalo Museum of Science, Buffalo, N. Y. cf. p. 18 19c; F-M, 20c; F-M

Cincinnati Art Museum, Cincinnati, Ohio cf. p. 19 N; F-M

Concordia Historical Institute, St. Louis, Mo. cf. p. 17 18c; F-M, 19c; F-M

Dwight-Barnard House, Deerfield, Mass. cf. p. 16 18c; F-M, 19c; F-M, 20c; F-M

House of Refuge Museum, Stuart, Fla. cf. p. 15 19c; M

Kamloops Museum Association, Kamloops, B. C. cf. p. 13 U-M

Montclair Art Museum, Montclair, N. J. cf. p. 18 U; F-M

Museum of Fine Arts, Boston, Mass. cf. p. 16 16c; C-F-M, 17c; C-F-M, 18c; C-F-M, 19c; C-F-M, 20c; C-F-M

Museum of Northern Arizona, Flagstaff, Ariz. cf. p. 13 19c; F-M, 20c; F-M

Museum of the American Indian, New York, N. Y. cf. p. 19 18c; F-M, 19c; F-M, 20c; F-M, N; F-M

Museum of the Fur Trade, Chadron, Nebr. cf. p. 17 19c; F-M, 20c; F-M

Museum of the Plains Indian, Browning, Mont. cf. p. 17 19c; F-M

Norwegian-American Historical Museum, Decorah, Iowa cf. p. 16 18c; F, 19c; F, N; F

Oakland Public Museum, Oakland, Calif. cf. p. 14 18c; F-M, 19c; F-M, 20c; F-M, N; F-M

Philadelphia Museum of Art, Philadelphia, Penna. cf. p. 20 18c; C-F-M, 19c; C-F-M, 20c; C-F-M

Ponca City Indian Museum,
Ponca City, Okla. cf. p.
20 19c; M, 20c; M
Valentine Museum, Richmond,
Va. cf. p.21 19c; C-F
Wadsworth Atheneum, Hart-
ford, Conn. cf. p.14 18c;
F-M, 19c; F-M, 20c; F-M
Witte Memorial Museum, San
Antonio, Texas cf. p.21
N; F-M

Headdress: Civil
United States-Canada
Beyer Home, Oconto County
Historical Museum, Oconto,
Wisc. cf. p.22 19c; M
Camden County Historical So-
ciety, Camden, N.J. cf.
p.18 18c; M
Manchester Historical Associ-
ation, Manchester, N.H.
cf. p.18 19c; M
Marine Historical Association,
Inc., Mystic, Conn. cf.
p.14 U; M
Mercer County Historical So-
ciety, Mercer Penna. cf.
p.20 18c; M, 19c; M
State Museum, Denver, Colo.
cf. p.14 19c; M, 20c; M

Headdress:Ecclesiastical-
Clerical
United States - Canada
Minnesota Historical Society Mu-
seum, St. Paul, Minn. cf.
p.17 19c; M
Museum of the Fur Trade,
Chadron, Nebr. cf. p.17
19c; M

Headdress:Ecclesiastical-Lay
United States - Canada
Greensboro Historical Museum,
Greensboro, N.C. cf. p.
19 19c; F-M
Pilgrim Society, Plymouth,
Mass. cf. p.17 17c; F
Shaker Museum, Old Chatham,
N.Y. cf. p.19 19c; F-M
Whaling Museum, New Bedford,
Mass. cf. p.16 19c; F-M

Headdress: Formal and Casual
United States - Canada
Arizona State Museum, Tucson,
Ariz. cf. p.13 19c; F-M,
20c; F-M
Beloit Historical Museum, Beloit,
Wisc. cf. p.21 19c; F-M
Bennington Historical Museum,
Bennington, Vt. cf. p.21 18c;
F-M, 19c; F-M
Beverly Historical Society, Bev-
erly, Mass. cf. p.16 19c;
F-M
Beyer Home, Oconto County His-
torical Museum, Oconto, Wisc.
cf. p.22 19c; F-M, 20c; F
Bostonian Society, Boston, Mass.
cf. p.16 19c; F-M
Boulder Pioneer Museum, Boulder,
Colo. cf. p.14 19c; F-M,
20c; F-M
Brick Store Museum, Kennebunk,
Maine cf. p.16 18c; F, 19c;
F, 20c; F
Buffalo Museum of Science, Buf-
falo, N.Y. cf. p.18 19c; F-
M, 20c; F-M
Camden County Historical Society,
Camden, N.J. cf. p.18 19c;
F-M
Carnegie Museum, Pittsburgh,
Penna. cf. p.20 19c; F-M
Charleston Museum, Charleston,
S.C. cf. p.21 18c; F, 19c;
F-M, 20c; F-M
Charles W. Bowers Memorial
Museum, Santa Ana, Calif. cf.
p.14 19c; F-M
Cincinnati Art Museum, Cincin-
nati, Ohio cf. p.19 N; F-M
Clay County Historical Society,
Moorhead, Minn. cf. p.17
19c; F-M, 20c; F
Colebrook Historical Society,
Colebrook, Conn. cf. p.14
19c; F-M, 20c; F
Concordia Historical Institute,
St. Louis, Mo. cf. p.17 18c;
F-M, 19c; F-M
Dallas Historical Society, Dallas,
Texas cf. p.21 19c; M
Danbury Scott-Fanton Museum and
Historical Society, Inc., Dan-

bury, Conn. cf. p.14 18c;
F, 19c; C-F-M
Delaware State Museum, Dover,
Del. cf. p.14 18c; F, 19c;
F, 20c; F
Detroit Historical Museum,
Detroit, Mich. cf. p.17
19c; F-M, 20c; F-M
Detroit Institute of Arts, De-
troit, Mich. cf. p.17 19c;
F
DeWitt Historical Society of
Tompkins County, Inc.,
Ithaca, N.Y. cf. p.19
19c; F-M
Dwight-Barnard House, Deer-
field, Mass. cf. p.16 18c;
F-M, 19c; F-M, 20c; F-M
East Hampton Historical So-
ciety, East Hampton, L.I.,
N.Y. cf. p.18 18c; F-M,
19c; F-M
E. M. Violette Museum, Kirks-
ville, Mo. cf. p.17 19c;
F-M, 20c; F-M
Erie Public Museum, Erie,
Penna. cf. p.20 18c; F-M,
19c; F-M
Greensboro Historical Museum,
Greensboro, N.C. cf. p.19
19c; F-M
Hall of History, Raleigh, N.C.
cf. p.19 18c; F-M, 19c;
F-M, 20c; F-M
Henry Francis du Pont Winter-
thur Museum, Winterthur,
Del. cf. p.14 18c; F
Historical Museum of Wabash
Valley, Terre Haute, Ind.
cf. p.15 19c; F-M, 20c;
F-M
Historical Society of York
County, York, Penna. cf.
p.20 19c; F-M
Holland Land Office Museum,
Batavia, N.Y. cf. p.18
18c; F-M, 19c; F-M, 20c;
F-M
Hood River County Historical
Museum, Hood River, Oreg.
cf. p.20 19c; F
House of Refuge Museum, Stuart,
Fla. cf. p.15 19c; M

Jacksonville Museum, Jackson-
ville, Oreg. cf. p.20 19c;
C-F-M
John Paul Jones House, Ports-
mouth, N.H. cf. p.18 19c;
F-M
Kansas City Museum Association,
Kansas City, Mo. cf. p.17
19c; F-M, 20c; F-M
Kenosha County Historical Mu-
seum, Kenosha, Wisc. cf.
p.21 19c; F-M
Lancaster County Historical So-
ciety, Lancaster, Penna. cf.
p.20 19c; F-M
Lennox and Addington County Mu-
seum, Napanee, Ont. cf. p.
13 19c; F
Los Angeles County Museum, Los
Angeles, Calif. cf. p.14 18c;
F, 19c; F-M, 20c; F-M
Manchester Historic Association,
Manchester, N.H. cf. p.18
19c; F-M
Marine Historical Association, Inc.,
Mystic, Conn. cf. p.14 U;
C-F-M, 19c; F
Mercer County Historical Society,
Mercer, Penna. cf. p.20 18c;
F-M
M. H. De Young Memorial Museum,
San Francisco, Calif. cf. p.
14 19c; F, 20c; F
Michigan State University Museum,
East Lansing, Mich. cf. p.
17 19c; F-M, 20c; F-M
Middlebury Historical Society,
Wyoming, N.Y. cf. p.19 19c;
F, 20c; F
Missouri Historical Society, St.
Louis, Mo. cf. p.17 18c; F-
M, 19c; F-M, 20c; F-M
Montclair Art Museum, Montclair,
N.J. cf. p.18 U; F-M
Museum of Fine Arts, Boston,
Mass. cf. p.16 16c; C-F-M,
17c; C-F-M, 18c; C-F-M, 19c;
C-F-M, 20c; C-F-M
Museum of History and Industry,
Seattle, Wash. cf. p.21 19c;
F-M, 20c; F-M
Museum of the American Indian,
New York, N.Y. cf. p.19 N;

49

F-M, 18c; F-M, 19c; F-M, 20c; F-M

Museum of the City of New York, New York, N.Y. cf. p.19 18c; C-F-M, 19c; C-F-M

Museum of the Fur Trade, Chadron, Nebr. cf. p.17 19c; F-M, 20c; F-M

Museum, National Society, Daughters of the American Revolution, Washington, D.C. cf. p.14 18c; F-M, 19c; F-M

Museum of the Plains Indian, Browning, Mont. cf. p. 17 19c; F-M

Nassau County Historical Museum, East Meadow, L.I., N.Y. cf. p.18 19c; F-M, 20c; F-M

Nebraska State Historical Society, Lincoln, Nebr. cf. p.18 19c; F-M, 20c; F-M

Nevada Historical Society, Reno, Nev. cf. p.18 19c; F-M

New Hampshire Historical Society, Concord, N.H. cf. p.18 19c; C-F-M, 20c; C-F-M

New Jersey Historical Society Museum, Newark, N.J. cf. p.18 19c; F-M

New Milford Historical Society, New Milford, Conn. cf. p.14 U; F-M

Norfolk Museum of Arts and Sciences, Norfolk, Va. cf. p.21 19c; F-M, 20c; F-M

Northampton County Historical and Genealogical Society, Easton, Penna. cf. p.20 U; F-M

Norwegian-American Historical Museum, Decorah, Iowa cf. p.16 18c; C-F-M, 19c; C-F-M, N; C-F-M

Nutley Historical Society Museum, Nutley, N.J. cf. p.18 19c; F

Oakland Public Museum, Oakland, Calif. cf. p.14 18c;

F-M, 19c; F-M, 20c; F-M, N; F-M

Ohio State Museum, Columbus, Ohio cf. p.20 19c; F-M

Old Sturbridge Village, Sturbridge, Mass. cf. p.17 18c; F-M, 19c; F-M

Oysterponds Historical Society, Inc., Orient, L.I., N.Y. cf. p.19 19c; C-F-M, 20c; C-F-M

Paramus Historical and Preservation Society, Ridgewood, N.J. cf. p.18 18c; F, 19c; F-M, 20c; C

Pejepscot Historical Society, Brunswick, Maine cf. p.16 19c; F-M

Pettigrew Museum, Sioux Falls, S.D. cf. p.21 18c; M, 19c; C-F-M, 20c; C-F-M

Philadelphia Museum of Art, Philadelphia, Penna. cf. p. 20 18c; C-F-M, 19c; C-F-M, 20c; C-F-M

Pilgrim Society, Plymouth, Mass. cf. p.17 17c; C-F

Pipe Spring National Monument, Moccasin, Ariz. cf. p.13 19c; F-M

Plymouth Antiquarian Society, Plymouth, Mass. cf. p.17 18c; F-M, 19c; F-M

Ponca City Indian Museum, Ponca City, Okla. cf. p.20 19c; M, 20c; M

Pope County Historical Society, Glenwood, Minn. cf. p.17 19c; F

Porter-Phelps-Huntington Historic House Museum, Hadley, Mass. cf. p.16 18c; F, 19c; M

Ringling Circus Museum, Sarasota, Fla. cf. p.15 19c; F-M, 20c; F-M

Rochester Museum of Arts and Sciences, Rochester, N.Y. cf. p.19 19c; C-F, 20c; F-M

Rocky Ford Museum, Rocky Ford, Colo. cf. p.14 19c; F

Royal Ontario Museum, Toronto, Ont. cf. p.13 18c; F-M, 19c; F-M, 20c; F-M

San Jacinto Monument and Museum, Houston, Texas cf. p. 21 19c; F
Shaker Museum, Old Chatham, N.Y. cf. p. 19 19c; F-M
Sleepy Hollow Restorations, Tarrytown, N.Y. cf. p. 19 18c; F
Stanton House, Clinton, Conn. cf. p. 14 19c; F
State Museum, Denver, Colo. cf. p. 14 19c; F-M, 20c; F-M
Swarthmore College, Friends Historical Library, Swarthmore, Penna. cf. p. 20 19c; F-M
Traphagen School of Fashion, Museum Collection, New York, N.Y. cf. p. 19 12c; F-M, 13c; F-M, 14c; F-M, 15c; F-M, 16c; F-M, 17c; F-M, 18c; F-M, 19c; F-M, 20c; F-M, N; F-M
Tryon County Muzzle Loaders, Inc., Fort Plain, N.Y. cf. p. 19 18c; F-M, 19c; F-M
University of Rhode Island, Costume and Clothing Collection, Kingston, R.I. cf. p. 20 19c; F-M, 20c; F-M
Valentine Museum, Richmond, Va. cf. p. 21 18c; C-F-M, 19c; C-F
Wadsworth Atheneum, Hartford, Conn. cf. p. 14 18c; F-M, 19c; F-M, 20c; F-M
Waterloo Library and Historical Society, Waterloo, N.Y. cf. p. 19 19c; F
Western Reserve Historical Society, Cleveland, Ohio cf. p. 20 19c; F-M, 20c; F-M
Whaling Museum, New Bedford, Mass. cf. p. 16 19c; F
Winnetka Historical Society, Winnetka, Ill. cf. p. 15 19c; F-M, 20c; F-M
Witte Memorial Museum, San Antonio, Texas cf. p. 21 N; F-M

Worcester Historical Society, Worcester, Mass. cf. p. 17 18c; F-M, 19c; F-M, 20c; F-M

Headdress: Military
United States - Canada
Beyer Home, Oconto County Historical Museum, Oconto, Wisc. cf. p. 22 20c; M
Clay County Historical Society, Moorhead, Minn. cf. p. 17 19c; M
Dallas Historical Society, Dallas, Texas cf. p. 21 19c; M
Greensboro Historical Museum, Greensboro, N.C. cf. p. 19 19c; M
Marine Historical Association, Inc., Mystic, Conn. cf. p. 14 U; M
Mercer County Historical Society, Mercer, Penna. cf. p. 20 18c; M
M.H.De Young Memorial Museum, San Francisco, Calif. cf. p. 14 19c; M
Museum of the Fur Trade, Chadron, Nebr. cf. p. 17 19c; M
Nassau County Historical Museum, East Meadow, L.I., N.Y. cf. p. 18 20c; M
Oysterponds Historical Society, Inc., Orient, L.I., N.Y. cf. p. 19 19c; M
Paramus Historical and Preservation Society, Ridgewood, N.J. cf. p. 18 19c; M
Royal Canadian Engineers Museum, Vedder Crossing, B.C. cf. p. 13 18c; M, 19c; M, 20c; M
San Jacinto Monument and Museum, Houston, Texas cf. p. 21 19c; M
United States Women's Army Corps Center, Fort McClellan, Ala. cf. p. 13 20c; F

Historical Clothing

Seventh Century
Coptic Tunics: Royal Ontario
Museum, Toronto, Ont.

Sixteenth Century
American Indian's Costume
Accessories: State of Alabama,
Department of Archives and
History, Montgomery, Ala. -
Earrings, bracelets, and
necklaces

Seventeenth Century
American Indian Costumes:
Rochester Museum of Arts
and Sciences, Rochester, N. Y.
American Indian Accessories:
State of Alabama, Depart-
ment of Archives and History,
Montgomery. Ala.
British Uniform Used by an
American Indian: Ponca City
Indian Museum, Ponca City,
Okla.
Chinese Ecclesiastical Vest-
ments of Taoist and Lamaist:
Royal Ontario Museum,
Toronto, Ont.
Jousting Costume: John Wood-
man Higgins Armory, Inc.,
Worcester, Mass.
Lances, Maces, and Pole
Arms: John Woodman Hig-
gins Armory, Inc., Worces-
ter, Mass.
Pilgrims' Clothing and Acces-
sories:
Bradford, Governor William.
Pilgrim Society, Plymouth,
Mass. - Red homespun cloak

Hopkins, Constance (May-
flower passenger). Pil-
grim Society, Plymouth,
Mass. - Felt hat with wide

brim and steeple crown

Standish, Miles. Pilgrim
Society, Plymouth, Mass. -
Baby cap and lace stomacher
worn by daughter, Lora

White, Peregrine (first white
child born in New England).
Pilgrim Society, Plymouth,
Mass. - Baby cap and bib

Winslow, Josiah. Pilgrim Society, Plymouth, Mass. - Baby
shoes

Winslow, Mrs. Josiah. Pil-
grim Society, Plymouth, Mass.
- Satin slippers and cape worn
by her at her marriage or by
her mother-in-law, Susannah,
widow of William White, at her
mariage to Edward Winslow
Quaker Costumes for Men and
Women: Rochester Museum of
Arts and Sciences, Rochester,
N. Y.
Texas Costumes: Witte Memorial
Museum, San Antonio, Texas -
Spanish-black lace and brocade

Eighteenth Century
American Indian Costumes and
Accessories: Museum of the
American Indian, New York,
N. Y.
Oakland Public Museum, Oak-
land, Calif.
State of Alabama, Department
of Archives and History, Mont-
gomery, Ala.
Ball Gowns: Valentine Museum,
Richmond, Va. - Belonging to
the wife of the U. S. President
Boggs, Captain John: College
Memorial Museum, Richmond,
Ky. - Revolutionary soldier's

52

uniform worn by him during the war and later in 1796 at his wedding

British Military Headdresses: Royal Canadian Engineers Museum, Vedder Crossing, B.C.

British Uniform: Danbury Scott-Fanton Museum and Historical Society, Inc., Danbury, Conn. - Worn by a soldier in the battle at Ridgefield, Connecticut, in 1777

Chasuble: San Jacinto Monument and Museum, Houston, Texas - Worn by Mexican Catholic priest

Chinese Ecclesiastical Vestments: Royal Ontario Museum, Toronto, Ont.

Connecticut State Militia Uniform: Danbury Scott-Fanton Museum and Historical Society, Inc., Danbury, Conn.

Dalmatic: San Jacinto Monument and Museum, Houston, Texas - White and gold, used on festive days

Fontbriand, Mgr. de: Notre Dame Church, Montreal, Que. - Ecclesiastical vestments-chasubles, stoles, and maniples worn by the Mgr.

French and Indian War Uniforms: Fort Ticonderoga, Ticonderoga, N.Y.

Hancock, John: Bostonian Society, Boston, Mass. - Cherry velvet coat with beige silk breeches

Le Ber, Jeanne: Notre Dame Church, Montreal, Que. - Hand embroidered dalmatics made by Mlle. Le Ber after she retired to a cell of the Notre Dame Church in 1728 at the age of 33. She was the daughter of a rich merchant, Jacques Le Ber

Monroe, James: James Monroe Law Office and Museum, Fredericksburg, Va. - His and his family's clothing

Naval Uniforms: York Institute, Saco, Maine

Norwegian Clothing: Norwegian-American Historical Museum, Decorah, Iowa - Worn by Norwegian pioneers in Iowa

Pioneer Woman's Wedding Gown: Boulder Pioneer Museum, Boulder, Colo.

Quakers' Costumes: Worcester Historical Society, Worcester, Mass.

Revolutionary War

Revolutionary Officers' Uniform: Oysterponds Historical Society, Inc., Orient, L.I., N.Y.

Charleston Museum, Charleston, S.C.

Revolutionary Soldiers' Uniform and War Clothing:
  Camden County Historical Society, Camden, N.J.
  Colebrook Historical Society, Colebrook, Conn.
  Essex Institute, Salem, Mass.
  Museum of the City of New York, New York, N.Y.
  Museum, National Society, Daughters of the American Revolution, Washington, D.C.
  New Milford Historical Society, New Milford, Conn.
  Paramus Historical and Preservation Society, Ridgewood, N.J.
  Quartermaster Museum, Fort Lee, Va.
  Tryon County Muzzle Loaders, Inc., Fort Plain, N.Y.
  United States Army Infantry Museum, Fort Benning, Ga.
  York Institute, Saco, Maine

Russian Orthodox Church Vestments: City Art Museum of St. Louis, St. Louis, Mo.

Spanish Religious Vestments: City Art Museum of St. Louis, St. Louis, Mo.

Stark, Major General John: Manchester Historic Association, Manchester, N.H. - Formal coat and trousers

Texan Costume: Witte Memorial Museum, San Antonio, Texas

Washington, President George:
Holland Land Office Museum,
Batavia, N.Y. - Cape given
by Washington to the wife of
a member of his staff

Old Court House Museum,
Vicksburg, Miss. - Knitted
sash belonging to Washington and later worn by Jefferson Davis

Dwight-Barnard House, Deerfield, Mass. - Wedding costume

Nineteenth Century
American Frontiersmen Costumes: Tryon County Muzzle
Loaders, Inc., Fort Plain,
N.Y. - Buckskin costumes
and women's calico dresses

Valentine Museum, Richmond,
Va. - Hunting and riding
clothes

Witte Memorial Museum, San
Antonio, Texas - Buckskin
costume of Texas frontiersman
American Indian Costumes:
Arizona State Museum, Tucson,
Ariz. - Apache Indian Costumes

Dallas Historical Society,
Hall of State, Dallas, Texas
- Vests, hats, and moccasins

House of Refuge Museum,
Stuart, Fla. - Seminole's
headdress, moccasins, leggings, shirt, dress, and
medicine coat

Museum of Northern Arizona,
Flagstaff, Ariz. - Hopi
clothing and masks

Museum of the American
Indian, New York, N.Y.

Museum of the Fur Trade,
Chadron, Nebr. - Sioux war
bonnet with full trail eagle
feather and Creek beaver

skin cap with beaded top

Museum of the Plains Indian,
Browning, Mont. - Plains and
Blackfoot Indian feather bonnets

Oakland Public Museum, Oakland, Calif. - Indian headdresses

Pettigrew Museum, Sioux Falls,
S.D. - Sioux Indian costumes
and moccasins

Ponca City Indian Museum,
Ponca City, Okla. - Indian
dance costumes and blankets

State of Alabama, Department
of Archives, Montgomery. Ala.
- Indian jewelry:earrings, bracelets, and necklaces
American Legion Suit: Beyer Home,
Oconto County Historical Museum, Oconto, Wisc.
Amoskeag Veteran's Uniform:
Manchester Historic Association,
Manchester, N.H.
Apache Indian Costumes: Museum
of Navajo Ceremonial Art, Santa
Fe, N.Mex. - Beaded buckskin
dress and jacket
Arapahoe Indian Costumes: Buffalo
Bill Museum, Buffalo Bill Historical Center, Cody, Wyo.
Banker's Wife's Dresses from
1880-90: Virginia City-Madison
County Historical Museum, Virginia City, Mont.
Baseball Uniforms: National Baseball Hall of Fame and Museum,
Inc., Cooperstown, N.Y.
Bishop's Skull Cap and Hat of the
Episcopal Church: Minnesota
Historical Society Museum, St.
Paul, Minn.
Blackfoot Indian's Costume: Museum
of the Plains Indians, Browning,
Mont.
Boston Hussars' Uniform (1810):
Bostonian Society, Boston, Mass.
British Regular Uniform of Red:
Guilford Courthouse National
Military Park, Greensboro, N.C.
Brittany National Costumes: Montclair Art Museum, Montclair, N.J.

Cadet's Uniform of Manchester, N. H.: Manchester Historic Association, Manchester, N. H.

Cheyenne Indian Costumes: Buffalo Bill Museum, Buffalo Bill Historical Center, Cody, Wyo.

Chinese Ecclesiastical Vestments: Royal Ontario Museum, Toronto, Ont.

Circus Costumes and Headdresses: Ringling Circus Museum, Sarasota, Fla.

Civil War Uniforms and Clothing:

Aurora Historical Society, Inc., Aurora, Ill.

Brick Store Museum, Kennebunk, Maine- Uniforms of officers and enlisted men

Buffalo Museum of Science, Buffalo, N. Y.

Camden County Historical Society, Camden, N. J.

Carnegie Museum, Pittsburgh, Penna.

Charleston Museum, Charleston, S. C.

Chicago Historical Society, Chicago, Ill.

Clay County Historical Society, Moorhead, Minn.

Colebrook Historical Society, Colebrook, Conn.

Davenport Public Museum, Davenport, Iowa

Essex Institute, Salem, Mass.

Greensboro Historical Museum, Greensboro, N. C.

Historical Museum of Wabash Valley, Terre Haute, Ind. - Northern officer's clothing

Historical Society of York County, York, Penna.

History Center of St. Lawrence County, Canton, N. Y.

Jefferson Davis Shrine and Museum, Biloxi, Miss. - Handmade uniform of Confederacy: Natchez fencible jacket

Lancaster County Historical Society, Lancaster, Penna. - Uniforms of Pennsylvania Volunteers and of a Civil War Major

Minnesota Historical Society Museum, St. Paul, Minn.

Montclair Art Museum, Montclair, N. J. - Union uniforms

Museum of City of New York, New York, N. Y.

Museum, National Society, Daughters of the American Revolution, Washington, D. C.

Nassau County Historical Museum, East Meadow, L. I., N. Y.

Old Fort Historical Museum, Fort Scott, Kans. - Captain's coat

Rochester Museum of Arts and Sciences, Rochester, N. Y. - Jackets, capes, overcoats for artillery, cavalry, and infantry

Rocky Ford Museum, Rocky Ford, Colo. - Uniforms of General Gabin

San Jacinto Monument and Museum, Houston, Texas - Uniform of Colonel Walter L. Mann

State Museum, State Historical Society of Colorado, Denver, Colo.

Tennessee State Museum, Nashville, Tenn.

Texas Memorial Museum, Austin, Texas - Uniform tunic

Tryon County Muzzle Loaders, Inc., Fort Plain, N. Y.- Union uniforms

Waterloo Library and Historical Society, Waterloo, N. Y.

Western Reserve Historical Society, Cleveland, Ohio

Witte Memorial Museum, San Antonio, Texas

Clay, Henry: Ashland, Lexington, Ky. - Coat and robe worn in 1814 at the Treaty of Ghent

Clay, Henry Mrs.: Ashland, Lexington, Ky. - Ruby red velvet dress

Clay, Henry Mrs., Jr.: Ashland,

Lexington, Ky. - Taffeta
dress
Cleveland, Grover Mrs.: Montgomery Museum of Fine Arts,
Montgomery, Ala. - Gown
Colfax, Schuyler Mrs.: Northern Indiana Historical Society, South Bend, Ind. - Jet
gown worn by Mrs. Colfax
when her husband was vicepresident
Comstock Period - 1860-80:
Nevada State Museum, Carson City, Nev. - Formal
gowns
Confederate and Union Civil
War Overcoats: E. M.
Violette Museum, Kirksville, Mo.
Confederate Uniforms: Jefferson Davis Shrine and Museum, Biloxi, Miss. - Hand
woven and handmade
Continental Uniform of American Army: Guilford Courthouse National Military
Park, Greensboro, N. C.
Copper-toed Boys Boots: E. M.
Violette Museum, Kirksville,
Mo.
Cowboy's Costume: Dallas Historical Society, Hall of
State, Dallas, Texas
Crockett, Davy: Alamo, San
Antonio, Texas - Beaded
buckskin vest
Crow Indian Costume: Buffalo
Bill Museum, Buffalo Bill
Historical Center, Cody, Wyo.
Davis, Jefferson:
Confederate Museum, Richmond, Va. - Suit of clothes

First White House of the
Confederacy, Montgomery,
Ala. - Slippers, dressing
gown, and a uniform made
of cloth woven in Virginia
and presented to him by
General Jubal Early

Jefferson Davis Shrine and
Museum, Biloxi, Miss. -
Wedding vest

Davis, Margaret: Jefferson Davis
Shrine and Museum, Biloxi,
Miss. - Wedding dress
Davis, Winnie: Jefferson Davis
Shrine and Museum, Biloxi,
Miss. - Evening dress and a
black taffeta dress
Doctor's High Hat: Oconto County
Historical Museum, Oconto,
Wisc.
Episcopal Bishop's Skull Cap and
Hat: Minnesota Historical Society Museum, St. Paul, Minn.
Episcopal Bishop's Vestments:
Minnesota Historical Society
Museum, St. Paul, Minn. -
Cassocks, stoles, and rochets
Eskimos Clothing - North and
South American: Museum of the
American Indian, New York, N. Y.
Fencible Jacket of Natchez worn
in Civil War: Jefferson Davis
Shrine and Museum, Biloxi,
Miss.
Fire Co. Volunteer Uniforms:
Charleston Museum, Charleston,
S. C.
Ford Theatre: Rochester Museum
of Arts and Sciences, Rochester,
N. Y. - Dress worn there the
night Lincoln was shot
Fraternal Lodge Uniforms: State
Museum, The State Historical
Society of Colorado, Denver,
Colo.
Gabin, General - Civil War General: Rocky Ford Museum,
Rocky Ford, Colo.
Glowacki, Major: Holland Land
Office Museum, Batavia, N. Y.
- Uniform worn by him in the
Polish revolution and worn on
arrival in U. S.
Governor of Wisconsin's Honor
Guard's Complete Uniform:
Beyer Home, Oconto, Wisc.
Governor's Aide in 1812: Bostonian
Society, Boston, Mass. - Uniform
Guerra, Anita De La - married
to Alfred Robinson in 1836,
described in Dana's Two Years
Before the Mast: Charles W.

Bowers Memorial Museum, Santa Ana, Calif. - Wedding dress

Hussars Uniforms: Bostonian Society, Boston, Mass. - Complete uniform of Boston Hussars of 1810

Inaugural Clothing: Minnesota Historical Society Museum, St. Paul, Minn. - Mrs. John S. Pillsbury's black lace formal reception gown worn at her husband's inauguration as Governor of Minnesota

Rochester Museum of Arts and Sciences, Rochester, N. Y. - Gown worn at President Buchanan's inauguration

Museum of Historic Costumes, Texas Women's University, Denton, Texas - Clothing belonging to the Presidents' and Governors' wives of Texas from 1886-1940

Jackson, Stonewall: Confederate Museum, Richmond, Va. - Uniform

Java Batik Sarong: Montclair Art Museum, Montclair, N. J.

Johnston, Joseph E.: Confederate Museum, Richmond, Va. - Uniform

Ku-Klux Klan Costumes: State Museum, The State Historical Society of Colorado, Denver, Colo.

Lafayette's Ball, New York, 1826: Ossining Historical Society Museum, Ossining, N. Y. - Striped mull worn at the ball

Laudsome Wedding Gown from 1860 and 1888: Northern Indiana Historical Society, South Bend, Ind.

Lee, General Robert E.: Confederate Museum, Richmond, Va. - Uniform

Lutheran Minister's Pulpit Robe: North Dakota Institute,

Fargo, N. D.

Mann, Col. Walter L.: San Jacinto Monument and Museum, Houston, Texas - Confederate Army uniform, pistol, and sabre

Militia Uniform: Bostonian Society, Boston, Mass. - Naval and Militia coats

Charleston Museum, Charleston, S. C. - Uniforms of South Carolina from 1870-1900

Moccasins of Tribes: Museum of the Fur Trade, Chadron, Nebr. - Arapahoe, Assiniboine, Bannock, Cheyenne, Chippewa, Navajo, Shoshone, Sioux

Monroe, James: James Monroe Law Office and Museum, Fredericksburg, Va. - Clothing belonging to him and his family

Navajo Indian Costume: Arizona State Museum, Tucson, Ariz.

New Hampshire National Guard Uniform: Manchester Historic Association, Manchester, N. H.

Norwegian Clothing: Norwegian-American Historical Museum, Decorah, Iowa - Worn by pioneers in America

Oriental Costumes: Pasadena Art Museum, Pasadena, Calif.

Paris Evening Gown: Texas Memorial Museum, Austin, Texas - Worn in days of the Republic of Texas

Pillsbury, Mrs. John: Minnesota Historical Society Museum, St. Paul, Minn. - Black lace formal reception gown worn at her husband's inauguration as governor

Plains Indian Costume: Arizona State Museum, Tucson, Ariz.

Planter Costumes: Maryland Historical Society, Baltimore, Md.

Polish Revolutionary Uniform: Holland Land Office Museum, Batavia, N. Y. - Worn by Major Glowacki

Political Campaign Hats: Manchester Historical Association, Manchester, N. H.

Pueblo Indian Costumes: Arizona State Museum, Tucson, Ariz.
Quaker Clothing:
Greensboro Historical Museum, Greensboro, N. C. - Headdresses

M. H. De Young Memorial Museum, San Francisco, Calif. - Dresses

Nassau County Historical Museum, East Meadow, L. I., N. Y. - Wedding dress and dresses, bonnets, and christening dresses

Whaling Museum, New Bedford, Mass. - Clothing and headdresses
Red Coat Cape of British Soldier: John Paul Jones House, Portsmouth, N. H. - Worn during the Revolutionary War
Rich Merchant Costumes:
Maryland Historical Society, Baltimore, Md.
Roman, André Bienvenu, Governor of Louisiana: Louisiana State Museum, New Orleans, La. - Wedding slippers worn by his daughter
San Jacinto, Battle of: San Jacinto Monument and Museum, Houston, Texas - Mexican uniform and a uniform of Col. Sidney Sherman
Scottish Highlanders Uniforms: M. H. De Young Memorial Museum, San Francisco, Calif.
Seminole Indians Medicine Man Costume and Moccasins of the Tribe: House of Refuge Museum, Stuart, Fla.
Sepulveda, Don Jose: Charles W. Bowers Memorial Museum, Santa Ana, Calif. - His clothing worn when French artist Henri Penelone painted his portrait in 1856
Shaker Sect Clothing: Shaker Museum, Old Chatham, N. Y. - Headdress and clothing
Sherman, Col. Sidney: San

Jacinto Monument and Museum, Houston, Texas - His uniform
Shoshone Indian Costumes: Buffalo Bill Museum, Buffalo Bill Historical Center, Cody, Wyo.
Sioux Indian Costumes and Accessories: Buffalo Bill Museum, Buffalo Bill Historical Center, Cody, Wyo. - Moccasins, beaded arm bands, blue cloth men's and women's leggings, solid beaded papoose carrier, dance bustle, L'Assomption wool sashes (hand and factory made), Winnebago sash (hand woven), silver disc mounted squaw belt, signal necklace with mirrors, medicine man's buffalo skin outfit, shawl, horned cap, anklets, and fur-wrapped staff
Southwestern Indian Costumes:
Museum of New Mexico, Santa Fe, N. Mex.
Spanish-American War Clothing and Uniforms:
Aurora Historical Society, Inc., Aurora, Ill.
Beyer Home, Oconto County Historical Museum, Oconto, Wisc.
Camden County Historical Society, Camden, N. J.
Carnegie Museum, Pittsburgh, Penna.
Colebrook Historical Society, Colebrook, Conn.
History Center of St. Lawrence County, Canton, N. Y.
Howard County Historical Society, Kokomo, Ind.
Jacksonville Museum, Jacksonville, Oreg.
Montclair Art Museum, Montclair, N. J.
Museum of the City of New York, New York, N. Y.
Oconto County Historical Museum, Oconto, Wisc.
Old Fort Historical Museum, Fort Scott, Kans.
Pettigrew Museum, Sioux Falls, S. D.

Tennessee State Museum,
Nashville, Tenn.
Waterloo Library and Historical Society, Waterloo,
N. Y.
Western Reserve Historical
Society, Cleveland, Ohio
Witte Memorial Museum,
San Antonio, Texas
Spanish-Colonial Costumes of
Southwestern United States:
Museum of New Mexico,
Santa Fe, N. Mex.
Stark, General John: Manchester Historic Association,
Manchester, N. H. - Formal
coat and trousers worn by
the general and dresses worn
by women of the family
State Guards' Uniform: State
Museum, the State Historical
Society of Colorado, Denver,
Colo.
Stuart, Major General James
E. B.: Confederate Museum,
Richmond, Va. - Uniform
Texas Navy: Texas Memorial
Museum, Austin, Texas -
Uniform of the commodore
Uniform of Aide of Massachusetts governor of 1812:
Bostonian Society, Boston,
Mass.
Uniform Worn at the Battle of
Lexington: Bostonian Society, Boston, Mass.
Uniforms of the Royal Canadian
Navy: Maritime Museum of
British Columbia, Esquimalt,
B. C.
United States Army Military
Accessories:
M. H. De Young Memorial
Museum, San Francisco,
Calif. - Cocked hat, hat
box, and dress hat

San Jacinto Monument and Museum, Houston, Texas -

United States Military Uniforms:
Quartermaster Museum,

Fort Lee, Va.
United States Army, Infantry
Museum, Fort Benning, Ga.
United State's Navy: Charleston
Museum, Charleston, S. C. -
Coat from the 1850's
Upton, General: Holland Land
Office Museum, Batavia, N. Y.
- Uniform worn by him as a
West Point general
Virginia City: Nevada Historical
Society, Reno, Nev. - Families'
clothing
Virginia Militia Uniforms; Guilford Courthouse National Military Park, Greensboro, N. C.
War of 1812: Camden County Historical Society, Camden, N. J.
- Clothing and uniforms

Carnegie Museum, Pittsburgh,
Penna. - Clothing and uniforms

Minnesota Historical Society
Museum, St. Paul, Minn. -
Red jacket of uniform
Wathall, General E. C.: Jefferson
Davis Shrine and Museum,
Biloxi, Miss. - His Confederate
uniforms
Wedding Dress of 1869 : La Casa
de Rancho Los Cerritos, Long
Beach, Calif. - Worn in San
Francisco
West Point Uniform: Holland Land
Office Museum, Batavia, N. Y.
- Worn by General Upton
Tennessee State Museum, Nashville, Tenn.
Winnetka Family: Winnetka Historical Society, Winnetka, Ill.
- Hats and bonnets
Worth, Chez: M. H. De Young
Memorial Museum, San Francisco, Calif. - Dress designed
by him

Nordica Homestead, Farmington,
Maine - Gowns designed by him
Zouave Uniform: Nassau County
Historical Museum, East Meadow,
L. I., N. Y. - Uniforms worn by
soldiers of certain infantry regiments in the French army. The

name comes from that of the Zouaoua tribe of Kabyles in Algeria, where Zouaves were first recruited in 1830

Twentieth Century

African Costumes from Southeast Africa Tribes: Witte Memorial Museum, San Antonio, Texas

Air Force Military Uniforms: Air Force Museum, Wright-Patterson Air Force Base, Dayton, Ohio

American Indians' Costumes: Marine Historical Association, Inc., Mystic, Conn.

Museum of Navajo Ceremonial Art, Santa Fe, N. Mex. - Navajo velvet blouse and cotton skirt

Museum of New Mexico, Santa Fe, N. Mex. - Apache costumes

Museum of Northern Arizona, Flagstaff, Ariz. - Hopi clothing and masks

Museum of the American Indian, New York, N. Y.

Museum of the Fur trade, Chadron, Nebr. - Sioux eagle feather war bonnet and red-dyed deerhair roach headdress

Ponca City Indian Museum, Ponca City, Okla. - Ponca woman's work dress and child's Indian grass skirt of Northwest Pacific

Apache Indian Costumes: Arizona State Museum, Tucson, Ariz.
Museum of New Mexico, Sante Fe, N. Mex.

Austrian Tyrolian Costumes: Montclair Art Museum, Montclair, N. J.

Baseball Uniforms: National Baseball Hall of Fame and Museum, Inc., Cooperstown, N. Y.

Brittany National Costumes: Montclair Art Museum, Montclair, N. J.

Bushonga Male Costume from the Belgian Congo: Witte Memorial Museum, San Antonio, Texas

Burmese Indian Costumes of Asia: Arizona State Museum, Tucson, Ariz.

Canadian Uniforms: Royal Canadian Engineers Museum, Vedder Crossing, B. C. - Belonging to military officers and nursing sisters

"Charro" Costumes of Mexico: Arizona State Museum, Tucson, Ariz.

Chinese Ecclesiastical Vestments of Taoist and Lamaist Churchmen: Royal Ontario Museum, Toronto, Ont.

Circus Costumes: Ringling Circus Museum, Sarasota, Fla.

Cora Indian Costumes of the Nayarit Area in Mexico: Arizona State Museum, Tucson, Ariz.

Cox, Lieutenant George: Lake County Historical Society, Tavares, Fla. - Flight suit and gloves belonging to the colonel who is the co-pilot who rescued Alan Shepard

Devalliéres, George and Maurice Denis: Notre Dame Church Museum, Montreal, Que. - Both men own an ecclesiastical cope embroidered for the Centennial of Notre Dame Church in 1929 by l'Atelier d'Art Sacré of Paris

Dior Gowns: M. H. De Young Memorial Museum, San Francisco, Calif.

Eskimos of North America and South America and their Costumes: Museum of the American Indian, New York, N. Y.

Gay Twenties Costumes: M. H. De Young Memorial Museum, San Francisco, Calif.

Haynes, Mrs. Elwood: Howard County Historical Society,

Kokomo, Ind. - Two dresses worn by her

Highland Maya Indian Costume of Guatemala in South America: Arizona State Museum, Tucson, Ariz.

Inauguration Clothing: Museum of Historic Costumes, Texas Women's University, Denton, Texas - Clothing belonging to the presidents' and governors' wives of Texas from 1886-1940

India, Sari, Benarest Costumes: Montclair Art Museum, Montclair, N.J.

Japanese Costumes: Witte Memorial Museum, San Antonio, Texas

Korean Contemporary Costumes: Witte Memorial Museum, San Antonio, Texas

Korean War Clothing and Uniforms: Minnesota Historical Society Museum, St. Paul, Minn.
State Museum, the State Historical Society of Colorado, Denver, Colo.

Militia Uniforms of New York: Rochester Museum of Arts and Sciences, Rochester, N.Y.

Navajo Indian Costumes: Arizona State Museum, Tucson, Ariz.
Museum of New Mexico, Santa Fe, N.M.

Northwestern Pacific Indian Tribe's Shredded Bark Skirts: Ponca City Indian Museum, Ponca City, Okla.

Notre Dame Ecclesiastical Copes: Notre Dame Museum, Montreal, Que. - Embroidered by l'Atelier d'Art Sacré of Paris, France, for the church's centennial

Nurses Uniforms of 1908: Minnesota Historical Society Museum, St. Paul, Minn.

Pueblo Indian Costumes: Museum of New Mexico, Santa Fe, N.Mex.

Quaker Clothing: Nassau County Historical Museum, East Meadow, L.I., N.Y. - Their dresses and wedding dresses, undergarments, night clothes, stockings, and shoes

Red Cross Uniforms: Carnegie Museum, Pittsburgh, Penna.
Minnesota Historical Society Museum, St. Paul, Minn.

Seminole Indian Costumes: Arizona State Museum, Tucson, Ariz.

Sioux Costumes and Headdresses: Museum of the Fur Trade, Chadron, Nebr. - Eagle feather war bonnet and red-dyed deerhair roach headdress

State Guard of Colorado Uniform: State Museum, the State Historical Society of Colorado, Denver, Colo.

Taylar, Mrs. of Bowling Green: Virginia City-Madison County Historical Museum, Virginia City, Mont. - Dresses designed by her during the period of 1900-05

Tyrolian Costumes: Montclair Art Museum, Montclair, N.J.

United States Military Uniforms: United States Army Infantry Museum, Fort Benning, Ga.

Winnetka Families' Hats and Bonnets: Winnetka Historical Society, Winnetka, Ill.

Women's Army Corps Uniforms-World Wars I and II: Boulder Pioneer Museum, Boulder, Colo.
Edith Nourse Rogers Museum, Fort McClellan, Ala.
Minnesota Historical Society Museum, St. Paul, Minn.

World War I-Clothing and Uniforms: Bennington Historical Museum, Bennington, Vt.
Beyer Home, Oconto County Historical Museum, Oconto, Wisc. - Doughboy helmet, German officer's helmet
Boulder Pioneer Museum, Boulder, Colo. - WAC uniforms
Brick Store Museum, Kennebunk, Maine

61

Buffalo Museum of Science,
Buffalo, N.Y.
Charleston Museum, Charleston, S.C. - U.S. Army
uniforms
Chicago Historical Society,
Chicago, Ill.
Clay County Historical Society, Moorehead, Minn.
Colebrook Historical Society,
Colebrook, Conn.
Dallas Historical Society,
Dallas, Texas - U.S. Army,
Navy, and Marine uniforms
Davenport Public Museum,
Davenport, Iowa
Delaware State Museum, Dover, Del.
E.M. Violette Museum, Kirksville, Mo. - U.S. Army
and Navy uniforms, nurses
uniforms, and German
officers' uniforms
Greensboro Historical Museum, Greensboro, N.C.
Historical Museum of Wabash
Valley, Terre Haute, Ind.
Historical Society of York
County, York, Penna.
Howard County Historical Society, Kokomo, Ind.
Liberty Memorial, Kansas
City, Mo.
Louisiana State Museum,
New Orleans, La.
Maritime Museum of British
Columbia, Esquimalt, B.C.
- Royal Canadian Navy
uniforms
Minnesota Historical Society
Museum, St. Paul, Minn.
Murray County Historical
Society, Slayton, Minn.
Museum of History and Industry, Seattle, Wash.
Nassau County Historical Museum, East Meadow, L.I.,
N.Y.
North Dakota Institute, Fargo,
N.D. - Navy ensign uniform
Norwegian-American Historical Museum, Decorah,
Iowa

Nutley Historical Society Museum, Nutley, N.J.
Oakland Public Museum, Oakland, Calif.
Oconto County Historical Museum, Oconto, Wisc. - German uniforms
Old Court House Museum,
Vicksburg, Miss.
Paramus Historical and Preservation Society, Ridgewood, N.J.
Pettigrew Museum, Sioux Falls,
S.D. - German officer's uniform
Quartermaster Museum, Fort
Lee, Va.
Red Cross National Headquarters
Museum, Washington, D.C. -
Army nurse and officer's
uniforms
Rochester Historical Society,
Rochester, N.Y.
Rochester Museum of Arts and
Sciences, Rochester, N.Y.
State Museum, the State Historical Society of Colorado,
Denver, Colo.
Tennessee State Museum, Nashville, Tenn. - Army, Marine,
and German uniforms
forms
United States Women's Army
Corps Museum, Washington,
D.C.
Valentine Museum, Richmond, Va.
Western Reserve Historical Society, Cleveland, Ohio
World War II - Clothing and Uniforms:
Bennington Historical Museum,
Bennington, Vt.
Boulder Pioneer Museum, Boulder, Colo. - W.A.C. uniforms
Carnegie Museum, Pittsburgh,
Penna. - American officer's
uniform
Charleston Museum, Charleston,
S.C. - U.S. Army officer's
uniform
Chicago Historical Society,
Chicago, Ill.
Colebrook Historical Society,
Colebrook, Conn.

Dallas Historical Society, Hall of State, Dallas, Texas - Army, Navy, and Marine uniforms

Davenport Public Museum, Davenport, Iowa

Delaware State Museum, Dover, Del.

E. M. Violette Museum, Kirksville, Mo. - U. S. Army and Navy uniforms, nurses' uniforms, German uniforms

Greensboro Historical Museum, Greensboro, N. C.

Historical Museum of Wabash Valley, Terre Haute, Ind.

Howard County Historical Society, Kokomo, Ind.

Louisiana State Museum, New Orleans, La.

Maritime Museum of British Columbia, Esquimalt, B. C. - Royal Canadian Navy uniforms

Minnesota Historical Society Museum, St. Paul, Minn. - W. A. C. uniforms

Museum of History and Industry, Seattle, Wash. - Army and Navy uniforms

Nevada Historical Society, Reno, Nev. - W. A. C. uniforms

Norwegian-American Historical Museum, Decorah, Iowa - German uniforms

Nutley Historical Society Museum, Nutley, N. J. - Red Cross uniforms of the Y. W. C. A.

Pettigrew Museum, Sioux Falls, S. D.

Quartermaster Museum, Fort Lee, Va.

Red Cross National Headquarters Museum, Washington, D. C. - Army Nurses' uniforms and officers' uniforms

Rochester Historical Society, Rochester, N. Y.

Rochester Museum of Arts and Sciences, Rochester, N. Y.

Royal Canadian Engineers Museum, Vedder Crossing, B. C. - Uniforms of the British and Canadian armies and nursing sisters

State Museum, the State Historical Society of Colorado, Denver, Colo.

Tennessee State Museum, Nashville, Tenn. - Army, Navy, Marine, and W. A. C. uniforms

United States Women's Army Corps Museum, Washington, D. C. - W. A. C. headdress and uniforms

Valentine Museum, Richmond, Va.

Zouave Uniforms: Rochester Museum of Arts and Sciences, Rochester, N. Y. - Worn by soldiers of certain infantry regiments in the French Army. The name comes from that of the Zouaoua tribe of Kabyles in Algeria, where Zouaves were first recruited in 1830.

Historical

National

African Costumes: Witte Memorial Museum, San Antonio, Texas

Apache Jewelry and Costumes: Arizona State Museum, Tucson, Ariz.

Arizona Pioneer Garments: Arizona Pioneer's Historical Society, Tucson, Ariz.

Asian Costumes: Witte Memorial Museum, San Antonio, Texas

Ch'ing Dynasty Chinese Costumes: Witte Memorial Museum, San Antonio, Texas

Cotton Palace Coronation Robes: Heritage Society of Waco, Waco, Texas

East Indian Brahman Caste Costumes and Baluchar Sari from Western Bengal: Witte Memorial Museum, San Antonio, Texas

Egyptian Costumes: Heritage Society of Waco, Waco, Texas

Famous Collection of Inaugural

Gowns: Cole County Museum, Jefferson City, Mo.

Formosa Costumes: Witte Memorial Museum, San Antonio, Texas

French Costumes: Texas Memorial Museum, Austin, Texas - Costume of the first teacher of European music in America, Pedro De Gante

Greco-Roman Coptic, and Ancient Peruvian Costumes: Textile Museum, Washington, D. C.

Greek Orthodox Church Vestments: Witte Memorial Museum, San Antonio, Texas

Haida Indians of the Queen Charlotte Islands Carved Bracelets of Silver Dollars: Museum of Northern British Columbia, Prince Rupert, B. C.

Hawaiian Girl's Missionary Inspired Costume: Niagara Falls Museum, Ltd., Niagara Falls, Ont. - Collar worth about $2,000 made of feathers from the extinct Kiwi and oo birds

Indian Costumes:
Arizona State Museum, Tucson, Ariz. - Navajo jewelry and costumes; North American Indians' costumes and jewelry; Plains Indians' jewelry and costumes; Pueblo Indians' jewelry and costumes; Yuman Indian jewelry and costumes

Heritage Society of Waco, Waco, Texas - Mayan costumes with train

Kamloops Museum Association, Kamloops, B. C. - Indian headdress of the Shuswap Tribe

Museum of the American Indian, New York, N. Y. - Eskimo sealskin costume; Far West and Southwest Indian's beaded papoose carrier, embroidered ceremonial shawl,
headdress of the antelope horn, headdress of rabbitskin and feathers; Plains and Plateau Indians' beaded buckskin dress, buckskin ghost dance shirt, feathered headdress and bustle, quilled moccasins and buckskin coat; Woodland and Northeast Indians beaded shoulder bag, mink midewiwin pouch and hood, painted caribou-skin coat, and quilled buckskin pouch

New York State Education Building, Albany, N. Y. - Iroquois Indian Costumes

Philbrook Art Center, Tulsa, Okla.

Southwest Museum, Los Angeles, Calif.

Witte Memorial Museum, San Antonio, Texas - Apache ceremonial costume, ghost dance shirt, headdresses, medicine man's headdress

India Bodices from the Western Provinces: Witte Memorial Museum, San Antonio, Texas

Japanese Costumes: Witte Memorial Museum, San Antonio, Texas - Wedding kimono, and Samurai suit of armor

Japanese Kasa Oho Ecclesiastical Vestment Costume: Museum of Art, Costume Center, Rhode Island School of Design, Providence, R. I.

Latin American Costumes: Witte Memorial Museum, San Antonio, Texas - Suit of lights, matador's costume; Women's Tehuantepec and Caxaco costumes

Maximillian: Witte Memorial Museum, San Antonio, Texas - Tilting suit

Norwegian Clothing and Accessories: Norwegian-American Historical Museum, Decorah, Iowa - Robes and Ruffs of the Church of Norway worn by pioneer pastors

Philippine Islands: Witte Memorial Museum, San Antonio, Texas -

Central Luzon, civilized and
mixed groups of Coastal
Luzon and mixed groups of
South Islanders clothing
Pilgrim, Quaker, Shaker, and
Amish Clothing: Essex
Institute, Salem, Mass.
Traphagen School of
Fashion, New York, N. Y.
Pre-Columbian South American
Man's Feather Headdress:
Museum of the American In-
dian, New York, N. Y.
Samurai Suit of Armor: Witte
Memorial Museum, San
Antonio, Texas
Siam Sarongs, Bodice, Silver
and Crystal Headdress and
Epaulets of the Temple
Dancers: Witte Memorial
Museum, San Antonio, Texas
South Pacific Lava-Lavas: Witte
Memorial Museum, San
Antonio, Texas

Jewelry

Jewelry Code

c - Century
F - Female
M - Male
U - Unclassified as to century

Jewelry
__United States - Canada__
Arizona State Museum, Tucson,
  Ariz. cf. p. 13   900-1500
  B. C.; F-M, U; F-M
Detroit Institute of Arts, De-
  troit, Mich. cf. p. 17
  19c; F
Henry Francis du Pont Win-
  terthur Museum, Winter-
  thur, Del. cf. p. 14 U; F
Kamloops Museum Association,
  Kamloops, B. C.   cf. p. 13
  U; F-M
La Casa de Rancho los Cer-
  ritos, Long Beach, Calif.
  cf. p. 13   19c; F
Lennox and Addington County
  Museum, Napanee, Ont.
  cf. p. 13   19c; F
Lotos Club, New York, N. Y.
  cf. p. 19   U; F-M
Museum of the American In-
  dian, New York, N. Y.
  cf. p. 19   18c; F-M, 19c;
  F-M, 20c; F-M
Museum of the Fur Trade,
  Chadron, Nebr.   cf. p.
  17   19c; M
Museum of Northern British
  Columbia, Prince Rupert,
  B. C.   cf. p. 13   U; F
Norwegian-American His-
  torical Museum, Decorah,
  Iowa   cf. p. 16   18c;
  F-M, N; F-M
Notre Dame Church, Montreal,
  Que.   cf. p. 13   17c; E-M,

18c; E-M
Pilgrim Antiquarian Society,
  Plymouth, Mass.   cf. p. 17
  17c; F
Rochester Museum of Arts and
  Sciences, Rochester, N. Y.
  cf. p. 19   19c; F-M
Rosicrucian Art Gallery, San
  Jose, Calif. cf. p. 14 N; F-M
State of Alabama Department of
  Archives and History, Mont-
  gomery, Ala.   cf. p. 13 16c;
  F-M, 17c; F-M, 18c; F-M,
  19c; F-M
Texas Memorial Museum, Aus-
  tin, Texas cf. p. 21 19c;
  F-M
Wadsworth Atheneum, Hartford,
  Conn.   cf. p. 14 19c; F-M
Witte Memorial Museum, San
  Antonio, Texas cf. p. 21 N;
  F-M

66

Military Uniforms and Accessories

Military Uniform and Accessory Code

c - Century
F - Female
M - Male
U - Unclassified as to century

Military Uniforms and Ac-
cessories
United States - Canada
Air Force Museum, Wright-
Patterson Air Force Base,
Dayton, Ohio cf. p. 20
20c; M
Aurora Historical Society,
Inc., Aurora, Ill. cf.
p. 15 19c; M
Bennington Museum, Benning-
ton, Vt. cf. p. 21 18c;
F-M, 19c; F-M, 20c; F-M
Beverly Historical Society,
Beverly, Mass. cf. p. 16
19c; M, 20c; M
Beyer Home, Oconto County
Historical Museum, Oconto,
Wisc. cf. p. 22 19c; M,
20c; M
Bostonian Society, Boston,
Mass. cf. p. 16 19c; M
Boulder Pioneer Museum,
Boulder , Colo. cf. p. 14
20c; F
Brick Store Museum, Kenne-
bunk, Maine cf. p. 16
19c; M, 20c; M
Brooklyn Museum, Brooklyn,
N. Y. cf. p. 18 N; M
Buffalo Museum of Science,
Buffalo, N. Y. cf. p. 18
19c; M, 20c; M
Camden County Historical
Society, Camden, N. J.
cf. p. 18 19c; M, 19c; M
Campus Martius Museum,
Marietta, Ohio cf. p. 20

18c; M, 19c; M
Carnegie Museum, Pittsburgh,
Penna. cf. p. 20 19c; M,
20c; M
Charleston Museum, Charleston,
S. C. cf. p. 21 19c; M, 20c;
M
Chicago Historical Society,
Chicago, Ill. cf. p. 15 19c; M,
20c; M
Clay County Historical Society,
Moorhead, Minn. cf. p. 17
19c; M, 20c; M
Colebrook Historical Society,
Colebrook, Conn. cf. p. 14
18c; M, 19c; M, 20c; M
Colonial Williamsburg, Inc.,
Williamsburg, Va. cf. p. 21
18c; M
Concordia Historical Institute,
St. Louis, Mo. cf. p. 17
18c; M, 19c; M
Confederate Museum, Richmond,
Va. cf. p. 21 19c; M
Dallas Historical Society, Dallas,
Texas cf. p. 21 18c; M, 19c;
M, 20c; M
Danbury Scott-Fanton Museum and
Historical Society, Inc., Danbury,
Conn. cf. p. 14 18c; M, 19c;
M
Davenport Public Museum, Daven-
port, Iowa cf. p. 15 19c; M,
20c; M
Delaware State Museum, Dover,
Del. cf. p. 14 20c; M
Detroit Historical Museum, Detroit,
Mich. cf. p. 17 19c; M, 20c;M

DeWitt Historical Society of
Tompkins County, Inc.,
Ithaca, N.Y. cf. p.19
19c; M
Dwight-Barnard House, Deer-
field, Mass. cf. p.16 18c;
M, 19c; M, 20c; M
E. M. Violette Museum, Kirks-
ville, Mo. cf. p.17 19c;
M, 20c; M
Erie Public Museum, Erie,
Penna. cf. p.20 18c; M,
19c; M
Essex Institute, Salem, Mass.
cf. p.17 18c; M, 19c; M
First White House of the Con-
federacy, Montgomery, Ala.
cf. p.13 19c; M
Florida State Museum, Gaines-
ville, Fla. cf. p.15 19c;
M
Fort Ticonderoga, Ticonder-
oga, N.Y. cf. p.19 18c;
M
Greensboro Historical Museum,
Greensboro, N.C. cf. p.
19 19c; F-M, 20c; F-M
Guilford Courthouse National
Military Park, Greens-
boro, N.C. cf. p.19
19c; M
Hall of History, Raleigh, N.C.
cf. p.19 18c; F-M, 19c;
F-M, 20c; F-M
Harvard College Library,
Cambridge, Mass. cf.
p.16 19c; M, 20c; M
Henry Francis du Pont Winter-
thur Museum, Winterthur,
Del. cf. p.14 19c; M
Historic Mobile Preservation
Society, Mobile, Ala. cf.
p.13 19c; M
Historical Museum of Wabash
Valley, Terre Haute, Ind.
cf. p.15 19c; M, 20c;
F-M
Historical Society of York
County, York, Penna.
cf. p.20 19c; M, 20c; M
History Center of St. Law-
rence County, Canton, N.Y.
cf. p.18 19c; M

Holland Land Office Museum,
Batavia, N.Y. cf. p.18 19c;
M
Howard County Historical Society,
Kokomo, Ind. cf. p.15 19c;
M, 20c; M
Jacksonville Museum, Jackson-
ville, Oreg. cf. p.20 19c; M
Jefferson Davis Shrine and Mu-
seum, Biloxi, Miss. cf. p.17
19c; M
Kamloops Museum Association,
Kamloops, B.C. cf. p.13
20c; M
Kansas City Museum Association,
Kansas City, Mo. cf. p.17
19c; F-M, 20c; F-M
Kenosha County Historical Museum,
Kenosha, Wisc. cf. p.21 19c;
M, 20c; M
Lake County Historical Society,
Tavares, Fla. cf. p.15 20c;
M
Lancaster County Historical So-
ciety, Lancaster, Penna. cf.
p.20 19c; F-M
Lennox and Addington County Mu-
seum, Napanee, Ont. cf. p.13
19c; M
Liberty Memorial, Kansas City,
Mo. cf. p.17 20c; M
Los Angeles County Museum, Los
Angeles, Calif. cf. p.14 18c;
M, 19c; M, 20c; M
Louisiana State Museum, New
Orleans, La. cf. p.16 19c;
M, 20c; M
Manchester Historic Association,
Manchester, N.H. cf. p.18
18c; M, 19c; M
Marine Historical Association, Inc.
Mystic, Conn. cf. p.14 19c; M
Maritime Museum of British
Columbia, Esquimalt, B.C.
cf. p.13 19c; F-M, 20c; F-M
Maryland Historical Society, Bal-
timore, Md. cf. p.16 18c;
M, 19c; M
Mercer County Historical Society,
Mercer, Penna. cf. p.20
18c; M, 19c; M
M. H. De Young Memorial Museum,
San Francisco, Calif. cf. p.14

19c; M

Michigan State University Museum, East Lansing, Mich. cf. p. 17 19c; F-M, 20c; F-M

Minnesota Historical Society Museum, St. Paul, Minn. cf. p. 17 19c; M, 20c; F-M

Morristown National Historical Park, Morristown, N. J. cf. p. 18 18c; F-M

Murray County Historical Society, Slayton, Minn. cf. p. 17 20c; M

Museum of History and Industry, Seattle, Wash. cf. p. 21 20c; M

Museum of New Mexico, Santa Fe, N. Mex. cf. p. 18 19c; M, 20c; M

Museum of the American Indian, New York, N. Y. cf. p. 19 18c; F-M, 19c; F-M, 20c; F-M

Museum of the City of New York, New York, N. Y. cf. p. 19 18c; M, 19c; M

Museum of the Fur Trade, Chadron, Nebr. cf. p. 17 19c; M

Museum, National Society, Daughters of the American Revolution, Washington, D. C. cf. p. 14 18c; M, 19c; M

Nassau County Historical Museum, East Meadow, L. I., N. Y. cf. p. 18 19c; M, 20c; M

Nebraska State Historical Society, Lincoln, Nebr. cf. p. 18 19c; M

Nevada Historical Society, Reno, Nev. cf. p. 18 20c; F-M

New Hampshire Historical Society, Concord, N. H. cf. p. 18 19c; F-M, 20c; F-M

New Jersey Historical Society Museum, Newark, N. J. cf. p. 18 19c; F-M

New Milford Historical Society, New Milford, Conn. cf. p. 14

18c; M

Norfolk Museum of Arts and Sciences, Norfolk, Va. cf. p. 21 19c; F-M, 20c; F-M

Northampton County Historical and Genealogical Society, Easton, Penna. cf. p. 20 U; M

North Dakota Institute, Fargo, N. D. cf. p. 19 20c; M

Norwegian-American Historical Museum, Decorah, Iowa cf. p. 16 19c; M, 20c; M

Nutley Historical Society Museum, Nutley, N. J. cf. p. 18 19c; F-M

Oakland Public Museum, Oakland, Calif. cf. p. 14 20c; F-M

Ohio State Museum, Columbus, Ohio, cf. p. 20 19c; F-M

Old Courthouse Museum, Vicksburg, Miss. cf. p. 17 20c; F-M

Old Fort Historical Museum, Fort Scott, Kans. cf. p. 16 19c; M

Old Sturbridge Village, Sturbridge, Mass. cf. p. 17 18c; M, 19c; M

Oysterponds Historical Society, Inc., Orient, L. I., N. Y. cf. p. 19 19c; M

Paramus Historical and Preservation Society, Ridgewood, N. J. cf. p. 18 18c; M, 19c; M, 20c; M

Pettigrew Museum, Sioux Falls, S. D. cf. p. 21 20c; M

Philadelphia Museum of Art, Philadelphia, Penna. cf. p. 20 18c; F-M, 19c; F-M, 20c; F-M

Ponca City Indian Museum, Ponca City, Okla. cf. p. 20 17c; M

Pope County Historical Society, Glenwood, Minn. cf. p. 17 20c; F-M

Quartermaster Museum, Fort Lee, Va. cf. p. 21 18c; F-M, 19c; F-M, 20c; F-M

Red Cross National Headquarters Museum, Washington, D. C. cf. p. 15 20c; F-M

Rochester Historical Society, Rochester, N. Y. cf. p. 19 19c; M, 20c; M

Rochester Museum of Arts and
Sciences, Rochester, N. Y.
cf. p. 19   19c; M, 20c; M

Rocky Ford Museum, Rocky
Ford, Colo.   cf. p. 14   19c;
M

Royal Canadian Engineers Museum, Vedder Crossing, B. C.
cf. p. 13   18c; M, 19c; M,
20c; F-M

Royal Ontario Museum, Toronto, Ont.   cf. p. 13   17c; M,
18c; M, 19c; M, 20c; F-M

San Jacinto Monument and Museum, Houston, Texas   cf.
p. 21   19c; M

Spanish Fort Museum, Pascagoula, Miss.   cf. p. 17
19c; M

State Museum, Denver, Colo.
cf. p. 14   19c; M, 20c; F-M

Tennessee State Museum,
Nashville, Tenn.   cf. p. 21
19c; M, 20c; F-M

Texas Memorial Museum,
Austin, Texas   cf. p. 21
19c; M, 20c; M, N; M

Tryon County Muzzle Loaders,
Inc. , Fort Plain, N. Y.
cf. p. 19   19c; M

United States Army Infantry
Museum, Fort Benning,
Ga.   cf. p. 15   18c; F-M,
19c; F-M, 20c; F-M

United States Women's Army
Corps Museum, Washington,
D. C.   cf. p. 15   20c; F

United States Women's Army
Corps Center, Fort Mc-
Clellan, Ala.   cf. p. 13
20c; F

Valentine Museum, Richmond,
Va.   cf. p. 21   18c; M,
19c; F-M, 20c; F-M

Wadsworth Atheneum, Hart-
ford, Conn.   cf. p. 14
18c; F-M, 19c; F-M,
20c; F-M

Waterloo Library and His-
torical Society, Waterloo,
N. Y.   cf. p. 19   19c; M

Western Reserve Historical
Society, Cleveland, Ohio

cf. p. 19   19c; M, 20c; M

West Point Museum, West Point,
N. Y.   cf. p. 19   U; M

Witte Memorial Museum, San
Antonio, Texas   cf. p. 21   19c;
M

Worcester Historical Society,
Worcester, Mass.   cf. p. 17
19c; M, 20c; M

York Institute, Saco, Maine
cf. p. 16   18c; M

National and Regional Clothing Code

c - Century
A - Casual clothing
B - Formal clothing
C - Children's clothing
E - Ecclesiastical Vestments
F - Female clothing
H - Headdress
J - Jewelry
M - Male clothing
N - National clothing
P - Professional uniforms
R - Regional clothing
S - Accessories
T - Civil uniforms
U - Unclassified as to century
X - Military clothing
Y - Armor
Z - Ceremonial clothing

National and Regional Clothing
Continent of Africa
North Africa
American Museum of Natural
History, New York, N. Y.
cf. p. 19 19c;

Carnegie Museum, Pittsburgh,
Penna. cf. p. 20 20c;
A-B-F-M

Royal Ontario Museum, Toronto,
Ont. cf. p. 13 U; A-B-F-M

Traphagen School of Fashion,
Museum Collection, New
York, N. Y. cf. p. 19 U;
A-F-M

Valentine Museum, Richmond,
Va. cf. p. 21 19c; 20c;
A-B-F-M

Continent of Asia
Arabia
Cincinnati Art Museum, Cincinnati, Ohio cf. p. 19

Valentine Museum, Richmond,
Va. cf. p. 21 20c; A-B-
F-M

Witte Memorial Museum, San
Antonio, Texas cf. p. 21
U; H

Asia
Museum of Fine Arts, Boston,
Mass. cf. p. 16 16c; 17c; 18c;
19c; 20c; A-B-C-E-F-H-M-S

Royal Ontario Museum, Toronto,
Ont. cf. p. 13 U; A-B-F-M

Traphagen School of Fashion,
New York, N. Y. cf. p. 19 U;
A

Burma
Arizona State Museum, University
of Arizona, Tucson, Ariz. cf.
p. 13 20c; A-B-F

China
American Museum of Natural History, New York, N. Y. cf. p.
19 19c

Baltimore Museum of Art, Baltimore, Md. cf. p. 16 U; A-B-
F-M

Buffalo Bill Museum, Cody,
Wyo. cf. p. 22 19c; A-B-
F-M-Z, 20c; A-B-F-M-S-
X

Buffalo Museum of Science,
Buffalo, N.Y. cf. p. 18
A-B-E-F-M-X

Carnegie Museum, Pitts-
burgh, Penna. cf. p.
20 20c; A-B-F-M

Charles W. Bowers Memorial
Museum, Santa Ana, Calif.
cf. p. 14 19c; A-B-F-H-
M-S

Cincinnati Art Museum, Cincinnati, Ohio cf. p. 19
19c; A-B-F-M

Concordia Historical Institute,
St. Louis, Mo. cf. p. 17
18c; 19c; A-B-F-H-M

Kansas City Museum Association, Kansas City, Mo.
cf. p. 17 U; A-B-F-M

Marine Historical Associ-
ation, Inc., Mystic, Conn.
cf. p. 14 19c; A-B-F-M-S

Montclair Art Museum, Montclair, N.J. cf. p. 18 U;
F-H-M

Oakland Public Museum,
Oakland, Calif. cf. p. 14
19c; A-B-F-M-S-X

Rochester Museum of Arts
and Sciences, Rochester,
N.Y. cf. p. 19 17c;
A-B-F-M

Royal Ontario Museum, Toronto, Ont. cf. p. 13
17c, 18c, 19c, 20c; A-B-
E-F-H-M-S-X

Valentine Museum, Richmond,
Va. cf. p. 21 19c, 20c;
A-B-F-M

William Rockhill Nelson
Gallery of Art, Kansas
City, Mo. cf. p. 17
17c; A-B-F-M-S, 18c;
A-B-F-M

Witte Memorial Museum, San
Antonio, Texas cf. p. 21
U; A-B-F-M-S

East India
Cincinnati Art Museum, Cin-

cinnati, Ohio cf. p. 19 19c;
A-B-F-M

Concordia Historical Institute, St.
Louis, Mo. cf. p. 17 18c,
19c; A-B-F-H-M

Montclair Art Museum, Montclair,
N.J. cf. p. 18 U; F-H-M

Valentine Museum, Richmond, Va.
cf. p. 21 20c; A-B-F-M

Witte Memorial Museum, San
Antonio, Texas cf. p. 21 U;
A-B-F-S

Egypt
Heritage Society of Waco, Texas
cf. p. 21 U; A-B-F-M

Lotos Club, New York, N.Y.
cf. p. 19 U; F-J-M

Rosicrucian Art Gallery, San
Jose, Calif. cf. p. 14 U;
F-J-M

Far East
Museum of New Mexico, Santa
Fe, N. Mex. cf. p. 18 19c,
20c; A-B-F-M

Formosa
Royal Ontario Museum, Toronto,
Ont. cf. p. 13 U; A-B-F-M

Indonesia
American Museum of Natural
History, New York, N.Y. cf.
p. 19 19c

Iran (Persia)
Witte Memorial Museum, San
Antonio, Texas cf. p. 21 U;
A-F-M

Israel
Valentine Museum, Richmond, Va.
cf. p. 21 20c; A-B-F-M

Japan
Carnegie Museum, Pittsburgh,
Penna. cf. p. 20 20c; A-B-
F-M

Charles W. Bowers Memorial
Museum, Santa Ana, Calif.
cf. p. 14 19c; A-B-F-M

Cincinnati Art Museum, Cincinnati,
Ohio cf. p. 19 19c; A-B-F-M

Costume Center, Museum of Art,
Providence, R.I. cf. p. 20
U; A-B-E-F-M

Marine Historical Association,
Inc., Mystic, Conn. cf. p. 14
19c; A-B-F-M-S

Oakland Public Museum, Oakland, Calif. cf. p. 14 19c; A-B-F-M-S-X

Rochester Museum of Arts and Sciences, Rochester, N. Y. cf. p. 19 17c; A-B-E-F-M

Texas Memorial Museum, Austin, Texas cf. p. 21 U; B-F-M

Valentine Museum, Richmond, Va. cf. p. 21 19c; 20c; A-B-F-M

William Rockhill Nelson Gallery of Art, Kansas City, Mo. cf. p. 17 17c, 18c; A-B-F-M

Java

Montclair Art Museum, Montclair, N. J. cf. p. 18 U; A-B-F

Korea

Rochester Museum of Arts and Sciences, Rochester, N. Y. cf. p. 19 17c; A-B-F-M

Valentine Museum, Richmond, Va. cf. p. 21 20c; A-B-F-M

William Rockhill Nelson Gallery of Art, Kansas City, Mo. cf. p. 17 17c; 18c; A-B-F-M

Witte Memorial Museum, San Antonio, Texas cf. p. 21 U; A-B-F-M-S

Malay

Historical Museum of Wabash Valley, Terre Haute, Ind. cf. p. 15 20c; A-F

Near East

Museum of New Mexico, Santa Fe, N. Mex. cf. p. 18 19c, 20c; A-B-F-M

Valentine Museum, Richmond, Va. cf. p. 21 20c; A-B-F-M

Witte Memorial Museum, San Antonio, Texas cf. p. 21 U; A-F-M

Orient

Pasadena Art Museum, Pasadena, Calif. cf. p. 14 19c;

A-B-F-M-S

Philadelphia Museum of Art, Philadelphia, Penna. cf. p.20 18c, 19c, 20c; A-B-E-F-H-M-X

Palestine

Valentine Museum, Richmond, Va. cf. p. 21 20c; A-B-F-M

Pakistan

Valentine Museum, Richmond, Va. cf. p. 21 20c; A-B-F-M

Siam (Thailand)

Witte Memorial Museum, San Antonio, Texas cf. p. 21 U; F-H-M-S

Siberia

American Museum of Natural History, New York, N. Y. cf. p. 19 19c

Syria

Witte Memorial Museum, San Antonio, Texas cf. p. 21 U; H

Tibet

Carnegie Museum, Pittsburgh, Penna. cf. p. 20 20c; A-B-F-M

Trans-Jordan

Valentine Museum, Richmond, Va. cf. p. 21 20c; A-B-F-M

National and Regional Clothing

Continent of Europe

General

Museum of Fine Arts, Boston, Mass. cf. p. 16 16c, 17c, 18c, 19c, 20c; A-B-C-E-F-H-M-S

Museum of New Mexico, Santa Fe, N. Mex. cf. p. 18 19c, 20c; A-B-F-M

Royal Ontario Museum, Toronto, Ont. cf. p. 13 18c, 19c, 20c; A-B-E-F-M-S

Traphagen School of Fashion, Museum Collection, New York, N. Y. cf. p. 19 U; A-F-M

Wadsworth Atheneum, Hartford, Conn. cf. p. 14 18c, 19c, 20c; A-B-C-E-F-H-J-M-S-X

Walters Art Gallery, Baltimore, Md. cf. p. 16 15c, 16c, 17c, 18c; A-B-E-F-M

Austria

Montclair Art Museum, Montclair, N. J. cf. p. 18 20c; A-B-F-M

Balkan Peninsula
Montclair Art Museum,
Montclair, N.J. cf.
p.18 18c; B-M
Royal Ontario Museum,
Toronto, Ont. cf. p.
13 U; A-B-F-M
Valentine Museum, Richmond,
Va. cf. p.21 19c, 20c;
A-B-F-M
France
Detroit Institute of Arts,
Detroit, Mich. cf. p.
17 19c; F-J-S, 20c;
A-B-C-F-M
Dwight-Barnard House, Deer-
field, Mass. cf. p.16
18c; H-F-M, 19c; 20c;
A-B-E-F-H-M-S-X
James Monroe Law Office
and Museum, Fredericks-
burg, Va. cf. p.21 18c,
19c; A-B-F-M
Los Angeles County Museum,
Los Angeles, Calif. cf.
p.14 15c; E-M, 16c;
B-E-F, 18c, 19c; A-B-E-
F-M-X, 20c; E-M
M. H. De Young Memorial Mu-
seum, San Francisco, Calif.
cf. p.14 17c; E-M, 19c;
B-F-X
Montclair Art Museum, Mont-
clair, N.J. cf. p.18 19c;
A-B-F, 20c; A-B-F-S
Nordica Homestead, Farming-
ton, Maine cf. p.16 19c;
B-F
Philadelphia Museum of Art,
Philadelphia, Penna. cf.
p.20 18c, 19c, 20c; A-B-
E-F-M-X-H
Valentine Museum, Richmond,
Va. cf. p.21 20c; A-B-
F-M
Germany
Cincinnati Art Museum, Cin-
cinnati, Ohio cf. p.19 U
Montclair Art Museum, Mont-
clair, N.J. cf. p.18 20c;
A-B-F
Great Britain
Colonial Williamsburg, Inc.,

Williamsburg, Va. cf. p.21
18c; A-B-F-M-P-X
Dwight-Barnard House, Deerfield,
Mass. cf. p.16 18c; F-H-M,
19c, 20c; A-B-E-F-H-M-S-X
Erie Public Museum, Erie, Penna.
cf. p.20 18c, 19c; A-B-E-F-
H-M-X
Los Angeles County Museum, Los
Angeles, Calif. cf. p.14 15c;
E-M, 16c; B-E-F, 18c, 19c;
A-B-E-F-M-X, 20c; E-M
Montclair Art Museum, Montclair,
N.J. cf. p.18 U; A-B-F
Philadelphia Museum of Art,
Philadelphia, Penna. cf. p.20
18c, 19c, 20c; A-B-E-F-H-M-X
Royal Canadian Engineers Museum,
Vedder Crossing, B.C. cf. p.
13 18c, 19c, 20c; F-H-M-P-X
Greco-Roman
Textile Museum, Washington, D.C.
cf. p.15 U; A-B-F-M
Hungary
Cincinnati Art Museum, Cincinnati,
Ohio cf. p.19 U
Italy
Fogg Art Museum, Cambridge,
Mass. cf. p.16 16c, 17c,
18c; E-M
Montclair Art Museum, Montclair,
N.J. cf. p.18 20c; C-F
Valentine Museum, Richmond, Va.
cf. p.21 20c; A-B-F-M
The Netherlands
Cincinnati Art Museum, Cincinnati,
Ohio cf. p.19 U
Rochester Museum of Arts and
Sciences, Rochester, N.Y. cf.
p.19 17c; A-B-F-M
Valentine Museum, Richmond, Va.
cf. p.21 19c, 20c; A-B-F-M
Norway
Norwegian-American History Mu-
seum, Decorah, Iowa cf. p.16
18c, 19c; A-B-C-E-F-H-J-M-
S-Z
Rochester Museum of Arts and
Sciences, Rochester, N.Y. cf.
p.19 17c; A-B-F-M
Roumania
Witte Memorial Museum, San
Antonio, Texas cf. p.21 U; A-F-

M
Scandinavia
Valentine Museum, Richmond,
Va. cf. p. 21 20c; A-B-
F-M
Scotland
M. H. De Young Memorial Museum, San Francisco, Calif.
cf. p. 14 19c; A-M-S
Montclair Art Museum, Montclair, N. J. cf. p. 18
19c; B-F
Niagara Falls Museum, Ltd.,
Niagara Falls, Ont. cf.
p. 13 U; A-B-F-M
Soviet Union
City Art Museum of St. Louis,
St. Louis, Mo. cf. p. 17
18c; E-M
Valentine Museum, Richmond,
Va. cf. p. 21 20c; A-B-
F-M
Spain
Charles W. Bowers Memorial
Museum, Santa Ana, Calif.
cf. p. 14 19c; F-S
City Art Museum of St.
Louis, St. Louis, Mo. cf.
p. 17 17c, 18c, 19c; E-M
Museum of New Mexico, Santa
Fe, N. Mex. cf. p. 18
19c; A-B-E-F-M-X
San Jacinto Monument and Museum, Houston, Texas cf.
p. 21 17c; A-B, 18c; A-E-M
Valentine Museum, Richmond,
Va. cf. p. 21 17c; A-B-
F-M, 20c; A-B-F-M
Witte Memorial Museum, San
Antonio, Texas cf. p. 21
15c; B-F
Switzerland
Valentine Museum, Richmond,
Va. cf. p. 21 20c; A-B-
F-M
Witte Memorial Museum, San
Antonio, Texas cf. p. 21
U; A-F-M
Turkey
Niagara Falls Museum, Ltd.,
Niagara Falls, Ont. cf.
p. 13 U; A-B-F-M
Witte Memorial Museum, San

Antonio, Texas cf. p. 21 U; S
Yugoslavia
Niagara Falls Museum, Ltd.,
Niagara Falls, Ont. cf. p. 13
U; A-B-F-M
Witte Memorial Museum, San
Antonio, Texas cf. p. 21 U;
B-F

National and Regional Clothing
Continent of North America
America
Cincinnati Art Museum, Cincinnati,
Ohio cf. p. 19 16c, 17c; A-B-
F-M
Concordia Historical Institute,
St. Louis, Mo. cf. p. 17 18c,
19c; A-B-F-H-M
Los Angeles County Museum, Los
Angeles, Calif. cf. p. 14 15c;
E-M, 16c; B-F-M, 18c, 19c;
A-B-E-F-M-S, 20c; E-M
Museum of Fine Arts, Boston,
Mass. cf. p. 16 16c, 17c,
18c, 19c, 20c; A-B-C-E-F-H-
M-S
Royal Ontario Museum, Toronto,
Ont. cf. p. 13 U; A-B-F-M
Wadsworth Atheneum, Hartford,
Conn. cf. p. 14 18c; A-B-E-
F-H-M-X, 19c; A-B-C-E-F-H-
J-M-X
Canada
Royal Canadian Engineers Museum,
Vedder Crossing, B. C. cf.
p. 13 18c, 19c, 20c; F-H-M-P-
X
Eskimo
American Museum of Natural History, New York, N. Y. cf. p.
19 19c
Marine Historical Association, Inc.,
Mystic, Conn. cf. p. 14 19c;
A-M-S
Museum of the American Indian,
New York, N. Y. cf. p. 19
18c, 19c, 20c; A-B-E-F-H-J-
M-P-X

National and Regional Clothing
Indian Clothing - American
American Museum of Natural History, New York, N. Y. cf. p.
19 19c

Detroit Institute of Arts, Detroit, Mich. cf. p. 17 20c; M-S

Montclair Art Museum, Montclair, N. J. cf. p. 18 U; A-B-F-M

Museum of Northern British Columbia, Prince Rupert, B. C. cf. p. 13 U; A-C-F-M

Niagara Falls Museum, Ltd., Niagara Falls, Ont. cf. p. 13 U; A-C-F-M

Oakland Public Museum, Oakland, Calif. cf. p. 14 18c, 19c; F-H-M-S-Z

Philbrook Art Center, Tulsa, Okla. cf. p. 20 U; A-B-F-M

Ponca City Indian Museum, Ponca City, Okla. cf. p. 20 19c; M-Z

Rochester Museum of Arts and Sciences, Rochester, N. Y. cf. p. 19 17c; A-B-F-M

State of Alabama, Department of Archives and History, Montgomery, Ala. cf. p. 13 16c, 17c, 18c; H-J

Valentine Museum, Richmond, Va. cf. p. 21 19c, 20c; A-B-F-M

Indian Clothing - Apache

Arizona State Museum, Tucson, Ariz. cf. p. 13 U; J, 19c, 20c; A-B-F-H-M

Museum of New Mexico, Santa Fe, N. Mex. cf. p. 18 19c, 20c; A-B-F-M-Z

Indian Clothing - Arapaho

Buffalo Museum of Science, Buffalo, N. Y. cf. p. 18 19c; A-B-F-M

Museum of the Plains Indian, Browning, Mont. cf. p. 17 19c; A-B-F-M-S-Z

Indian Clothing - Blackfoot

Museum of the Plains Indian, Browning, Mont. cf. p. 17 19c; A-B-F-M-S-Z

Indian Clothing - Charro

Arizona State Museum, Tucson, Ariz. cf. p. 13 20c; A-B-F-H-M

Indian Clothing - Cheyenne

Buffalo Museum of Science, Buffalo, N. Y. cf. p. 18 19c; A-B-F-M

Museum of the Plains Indian, Browning, Mont. cf. p. 17 19c; A-B-F-M-S-Z

Indian Clothing - Cora

Arizona State Museum, Tucson, Ariz. cf. p. 13 20c; A-B-F-H-M

Indian Clothing - Crow

Buffalo Museum of Science, Buffalo, N. Y. cf. p. 18 19c; A-B-F-M

Museum of the Plains Indian, Browning, Mont. cf. p. 17 19c; A-B-F-M-S-Z

Indian Clothing - Haida

Museum of Northern British Columbia, Prince Rupert, B. C. cf. p. 13 U; F-J

Indian Clothing - Hopi

Museum of Northern Arizona, Flagstaff, Ariz. cf. p. 13 19c; 20c; A-B-F-M

Indian Clothing - Iroquois

Museum of Art, Albany, N. Y. cf. p. 18 U; A-B-F-M

Indian Clothing - Mayan

Heritage Society of Waco, Waco, Texas cf. p. 21 U; B-F

Arizona State Museum, Tucson, Ariz. cf. p. 13 20c; A-B-F-H-M

Indian Clothing - Navajo

Arizona State Museum, Tucson, Ariz. cf. p. 13 U; J, 19c; A-B-F-M, 20c; A-B-F-H-M

Museum of Navajo Ceremonial Art, Santa Fe, N. Mex. cf. p. 18 20c; A-B-F

Museum of New Mexico, Santa Fe, N. Mex. cf. p. 18 19c, 20c; A-B-F-M-Z

Indian Clothing - Pueblo

Arizona State Museum, Tucson, Ariz. cf. p. 13 U; J, 19c; A-B-F-M

Museum of New Mexico, Santa Fe, N. Mex. cf. p. 18 19c,

76

20c; A-B-F-M-Z

Indian Clothing - Seminole

Arizona State Museum, Tucson,
Ariz. cf. p.13 20c; A-B-
F-H-M

House of Refuge Museum,
Stuart, Fla. cf. p.15 19c;
A-B-F-H-M-S-Z

Indian Clothing - Shoshone

Buffalo Museum of Science,
Buffalo, N.Y. cf. p.18
19c; A-B-F-M

Museum of the Plains Indian,
Browning, Mont. cf. p.17
19c; A-B-F-M-S-Z

Indian Clothing - Shuswap

Kamloops Museum Association,
Kamloops, B.C. cf. p.13
U; H-M-J

Indian Clothing - Sioux

Buffalo Museum of Science,
Buffalo, N.Y. cf. p.18
19c; A-B-F-M

Museum of the Fur Trade,
Chadron, Nebr. cf. p.17
U; H-M

Museum of the Plains Indian,
Browning, Mont. cf. p.17
19c; A-B-F-M-S-Z

Pettigrew Museum, Sioux
Falls, S.D. cf. p.21
19c; A-B-E-F-H-M-S

Indian Clothing - Yuman

Arizona State Museum, Tucson, Ariz. cf. p.13 U; J

National and Regional Clothing
    Mexico

Museum of New Mexico, Santa
Fe, N.Mex. cf. p.18 U;
A-B-E-F-M

Valentine Museum, Richmond,
Va. cf. p.21 20c; A-B-
F-M

Witte Memorial Museum, San
Antonio, Texas cf. p.21
U

National and Regional Clothing
    United States
        Alaska

Valentine Museum, Richmond,
Va. cf. p.21 19c; 20c;
A-B-F-M

Hawaii

Niagara Falls Museum, Ltd.,
Niagara Falls, Ont. cf. p.
13 U; C-F

New England

Florida State Museum, Gainesville, Fla. cf. p.15 19c; B-
F-Z

John Paul Jones House, Portsmouth, N.H. cf. p.18 18c;
A-B-F-M-S, 19c; A-B-F-H-M-S

New Hampshire Historical Society,
Concord, N.H. cf. p.18 19c,
20c; A-B-C-D-F-M

Old Sturbridge Village, Sturbridge,
Mass. cf. p.17 18c, 19c;
A-B-F-H-M-S-X

Plymouth Antiquarian Society,
Plymouth, Mass. cf. p.17
18c, 19c; A-B-F-H-M-S

Porter-Phelps-Huntington Foundation, Hadley, Mass. cf. p.16
18c, 19c; A-B-F-M-S

Portsmouth Historical Society,
Portsmouth, R.I. cf. p.18
U; A-B-F-M

Central Northeast

American Museum of City of New
York, N.Y. cf. p.19 18c, 19c;
A-B-F-M-S-X

Lancaster County Historical Society, Lancaster, Penna. cf.
p.20 19c; A-B-F-M-S-X

New Jersey Historical Society,
Newark, N.J. cf. p.18 19c;
A-B-F-H-M-P-S-X

Pennsylvania Farm Museum of Landis Valley, Lancaster, Penna.
cf. p.20 19c, 20c; A-B-C-F-M

Central Northwest

Nebraska State Historical Society,
Lincoln, Nebr. cf. p.18 19c;
B-F-H-M-S-X

Nevada State Museum, Carson City,
Nev. cf. p.18 19c; A-B-F

Midwest

Campus Martius Museum, Marietta,
Ohio cf. p.20 18c, 19c; A-B-
F-M-S-X

Michigan State University Museum,
East Lansing, Mich. cf. p.17
19c, 20c; A-B-F-M-S-X

Norwegian American Historical

Museum, Decorah, Iowa
cf. p. 16 U; A-B-C-E-
F-H-J-M-S-Z
Ohio State Museum, Columbus,
Ohio cf. p. 20 19c; F-H-
M-P-S-X
Olmsted County Historical So-
ciety, Rochester, Minn.
cf. p. 17 19c, 20c; A-B-F
South
Louisiana State Museum, New
Orleans, La. cf. p. 16
19c, 20c; A-B-F-M-S-X
Southwest
Arizona State Museum, Tucson,
Ariz. cf. p. 13 19c, 20c;
A-B-F-H-M
Museum of New Mexico, Santa
Fe, N. Mex. cf. p. 18 U;
A-B-E-F-M
Ponca City Indian Museum,
Ponca City, Okla. cf. p.
20 20c; B-F
Witte Memorial Museum, San
Antonio, Texas cf. p. 21
18c; A-B-C-F-M
Far West
Jacksonville Museum, Jack-
sonville, Oreg. cf. p. 20
19c; A-B-E-H-M-P-S-X
Los Angeles County Museum,
Los Angeles, Calif. cf.
p. 14 18c, 19c; A-B-E-F-
M-S

National and Regional Clothing
Miscellaneous
Amish
Traphagen School of Fashion,
Museum Collection, New
York, N. Y. cf. p. 19
U; A-F-M
Circus
Ringling Circus Museum,
Sarasota, Fla. cf. p. 15
20c; F-H-M
Frontiermen
Tryon County Muzzle Loaders,
Inc. , Fort Plain, N. Y.
cf. p. 19 18c, 19c; A-C-
F-H-M-X
Valentine Museum, Richmond,
Va. cf. p. 21 17c, 18c,

19c; A-B-C-F-M-S-X
Protestant Missionary
Hawaiian Mission Children's So-
ciety, Honolulu, Hawaii cf.
p. 15 19c; A-F-M-S
Pilgrim
Essex Institute, Salem, Mass.
cf. p. 17 17c; A-B-F-M
Plymouth Antiquarian Society,
Plymouth, Mass. cf. p. 17
17c; A-B-C-F-M-S
Pioneer
Allen County Museum, Lima, Ohio
cf. p. 20 19c; A-B-F-M
Arizona Pioneers' Historical So-
ciety, Tucson, Ariz. cf. p.
13 U; A-B-F-M
Boulder Pioneer Museum, Boulder,
Colo. cf. p. 14 17c, 18c; B-F
La Casa de Rancho los Cerritos,
Long Beach, Calif. cf. p. 13
19c; A-B-F-J-S
Kamloops Museum Association,
Kamloops, B. C. cf. p. 13 19c,
20c; A-B-F-M-S-X
Shaker
Shaker Museum, Old Chatham,
N. Y. cf. p. 19 19c; A-F-H-M
Society of the Friends
Essex Institute, Salem, Mass.
cf. p. 17 U; A-B-F-M
Greensboro Historical Museum,
Greensboro, N. C. cf. p. 19
19c; H
M. H. De Young Memorial Museum,
San Francisco, Calif. cf. p.
14 19c; A-F
Nassau County Historical Museum,
East Meadow, L. I. , N. Y. cf.
p. 18 19c, 20c; A-B-F-S
Rochester Museum of Arts and
Sciences, Rochester, N. Y. cf.
p. 19 17c; A-B-F-M
Traphagen School of Fashion, New
York, N. Y. cf. p. 19 U; A-F-
M
Whaling Museum, New Bedford,
Mass. cf. p. 16 19c; B-F-S-H
Worcester Historical Society,
Worcester, Mass. cf. p. 17
18c; A-B-C-F-M

National and Regional Clothing
  Central America
    Guatemala
Rochester Museum of Arts and
  Sciences, Rochester, N.Y.
  cf. p. 19   17c; A-B-F-M

National and Regional Clothing
  South America
    Boliva
Valentine Museum, Richmond,
  Va.   cf. p. 21   19c, 20c;
  A-B-F-M
Brazil
Valentine Museum, Richmond,
  Va.   cf. p. 21   19c, 20c;
  A-B-F-M
Ecuador
Valentine Museum, Richmond,
  Va.   cf. p. 21   20c; A-B-
  F-M
Eskimo
Museum of the American In-
  dian, New York, N.Y.   cf.
  p. 19   18c; A-B-E-F-J-S-X
Peru
Textile Museum, Washington,
  D.C.   cf. p. 15   U; A-B-
  F-M
Pre-Columbia
Museum of the American In-
  dian, New York, N.Y.   cf.
  p. 19   U; H

Professional Uniforms

United States

Eighteenth Century
Italian opera costumes from "La Serva Padrona": John and Mable Ringling Museum of Art, Sarasota, Fla.
Physician's costume: Harrison Gray Otis House, Boston, Mass.

Nineteenth Century
Baseball uniforms: National Baseball Hall of Fame and Museum, Inc., Cooperstown, N. Y.
Boy Scout master's overcoat and uniform blouse: Nassau County Historical Museum, East Meadow, L. I., N. Y.
Circus costumes: Ringling Circus Museum, Sarasota, Fla.
Doctor's gown: Nassau County Historical Museum, East Meadow, L. I., N. Y.
Doctor's high hat: Beyer Home, Oconto County Historical Society, Oconto, Wisc.
Fire company volunteer uniforms: Charleston Museum, Charleston, S. C.
Grand Opera costumes of the famous diva, Lillian Nordica: Nordica Homestead, Farmington, Maine
Missionary clothing: Hawaiian Mission Children's Society, Honolulu, Hawaii
Nurse's uniform: Beverly Historical Society, Beverly, Mass.
 Detroit Historical Museum, Detroit, Mich.
 Museum of History and In-

dustry, Seattle, Wash.
Opera costumes: Historical Museum of Wabash Valley, Terre Haute, Ind.
Red Cross uniform: Nutley Historical Society Museum, Nutley, N. J.
Theatrical costumes - Cap and ruff worn by Mme. Modjeska in the role of Mary Stuart. Bracelets and high gold kid laced sandals worn in Cleopatra. Charles W. Bowers Memorial Museum, Santa Ana, Calif.
Theatrical costumes - Cape and dress worn by Alice Fischer Harcourt in "School for Husbands": Sheldon Swope Art Gallery, Terre Haute, Ind.
Theatrical costumes - Costumes of Alice Neilson: Kansas City Museum Association, Kansas City, Mo.
Theatrical costumes - "Big Heads": Ringling Circus Museum, Sarasota, Fla.
Theatrical costumes - Vaudeville and opera costumes: Historical Museum of Wabash Valley, Terre Haute, Ind.

Twentieth Century
Academic robe with academic hat. Minister Prince Albert. Beyer Home, Oconto County Historical Museum, Oconto, Wisc.
Baseball uniforms: National Baseball Hall of Fame and Museum, Inc., Cooperstown, N. Y.
Brownie's uniform. Campfire Girl's uniform: Rochester Museum of Arts and Sciences,

Rochester, N. Y.

Circus costumes and "Big Heads": Ringling Circus Museum, Sarasota, Fla.

College girl's uniform: Rochester Museum of Arts and Sciences, Rochester, N. Y.

Grey Lady uniforms: Minnesota Historical Society Museum, St. Paul, Minn.

Maid's uniform: Rochester Museum of Arts and Sciences, Rochester, N. Y.

Matador's costume: Witte Memorial Museum, San Antonio, Texas

Nurses uniforms:
Detroit Historical Museum, Detroit, Mich.
E. M. Violette Museum, Kirksville, Mo.
Minnesota Historical Society Museum, St. Paul, Minn.
Museum of History and Industry, Seattle, Wash.

Peyote Men's costumes: Ponca City Indian Museum, Ponca City, Okla.

Red Cross uniforms- female:
Carnegie Museum, Pittsburgh, Penna.
Minnesota Historical Society Museum, St. Paul, Minn.
Red Cross National Headquarters Museum, Washington, D. C.
Rochester Museum of Arts and Sciences, Rochester, N. Y.

Red Cross Public Health Nurses uniforms. Red Cross Volunteer uniforms: Red Cross National Headquarters Museum, Washington, D. C.

Secretary's costume: Rochester Museum of Arts and Sciences, Rochester, N. Y.

Theatrical costumes:
American Museum of Comedy, Crestwood, N. Y.
Harvard College Library, Cambridge, Mass.
Historical Museum of Wabash Valley, Terre Haute, Inc.
Ringling Circus Museum, Sarasota, Fla.

Vaudeville and opera costumes: Historical Museum of Wabash Valley, Terre Haute, Ind.

Clothing Terms

Accessories

Baby Carrier-Indian beaded: Museum of the American Indian, New York, N. Y. cf. p. 19 N

Chatelaines-handbag: Valentine Museum, Richmond, Va. cf. p. 21 19c

Dance Bustle-Feathered Indian: Museum of the American Indian, New York, N. Y. cf. p. 19 N

Fans - Japanese: Marine Historical Association, Inc., Mystic, Conn. cf. p. 14 19c

Fans - Victorian: Marine Historical Association, Inc., Mystic, Conn. cf. p. 14 19c

Hoops: Spanish Fort Museum, Pascagoula, Miss. cf. p. 17 19c

Indian Pouches - Beaded Mink Midewiwin: Museum of the American Indian, New York, N. Y. cf. p. 19 N

Indian Pouches - Quilled Buckskin: Museum of the American Indian, New York, N. Y. cf. p. 19 N

Lorgnettes-eye glasses: Valentine Museum, Richmond, Va. cf. p. 21 18c

Mitts for women:
Charles W. Bowers Memorial Museum, Santa Ana, Calif. cf. p. 14 19c
Nassau County Historical Museum, East Meadow, L. I., N. Y. cf. p. 18 19c
Plymouth Antiquarian Society, Plymouth, Mass. cf. p. 17 17c
Valentine Museum, Richmond,

Va. cf. p. 21 19c

Mitts for women- Lace: Rocky Ford Museum, Rocky Ford, Colo. cf. p. 14 19c

Muffs:
Paramus Historical and Preservation Society, Ridgewood, N. J. cf. p. 18 20c
Valentine Museum, Richmond, Va. cf. p. 21 19c

Muffs - Fur: Nassau County Historical Museum, East Meadow, L. I., N. Y. cf. p. 18

Parasols:
Marine Historical Association, Mystic, Conn. cf. p. 14 19c
Rochester Museum of Arts and Sciences, Rochester, N. Y. cf. p. 19 19c
Valentine Museum, Richmond, Va. cf. p. 21 18c; 19c

Parasols - Mourning: Ossining Historical Society Museum, Ossining, N. Y. cf. p. 19 19c

Pinafores: Valentine Museum, Richmond, Va. cf. p. 21 18c; 19c

Ruffs - Of the Church of Norway and worn by pioneer pastors: Norwegian-American Historical Museum, Decorah, Iowa cf. p. 16 19c

Ruffs - Worn by women: Charles W. Bowers Memorial Museum, Santa Ana, Calif. cf. p. 14 19c

Serapes: Carnegie Museum, Pittsburgh, Penna. cf. p. 20 20c

Shawls - Mourning: Ossining Historical Society Museum, Ossining, N. Y. cf. p. 19 19c

Shawls - Paisley:
East Hampton Historical Society, East Hampton, L. I., N. Y. cf. p. 18 19c
Historical Museum of Wabash

Detroit Institute of Arts,
Detroit, Mich. cf. p.
17 19c
M. H. De Young Memorial
Museum, San Francisco,
Calif. cf. p. 14 17c; 18c
Notre Dame Church, Montreal,
Que. cf. p. 13 17c
San Jacinto Monument and
Museum, Houston, Texas
cf. p. 21 18c
Copes: Notre Dame Church,
Montreal, Que. cf. p. 13
20c
Dalmatics:
Detroit Institute of Arts,
Detroit, Mich. cf. p. 17
19c
Notre Dame Church, Mont-
real, Que. cf. p. 13 U
San Jacinto Monument and
Museum, Houston, Texas
cf. p. 21 18c
Japanese Kesa and Ohi: Museum
of Art, Rhode Island School
of Design, Providence, R. I.
cf. p. 20 U
Maniples: Notre Dame Church,
Montreal, Que. cf. p. 13 U
Orpheys-ecclesiastical woven:
Detroit Institute of Arts,
Detroit, Mich. cf. p. 17 19c
Russian Orthodox Church
Vestments: City Art Museum
of St. Louis, St. Louis, Mo.
cf. p. 17 19c
Shaker Costumes and Headdress:
Shaker Museum, Old Chatham,
N. Y. cf. p. 19 19c
Stoles: Notre Dame Church,
Montreal, Que. cf. p. 13 U

Footwear
Boots - Coppertoed: E. M.
Violette Museum, Kirks-
ville, Mo. cf. p. 17 19c
Boots - Sealskin: Marine His-
torical Association, Inc.,
Mystic, Conn. cf. p. 14
Moccasins - Indian:
Dallas Historical Society,
Dallas, Texas cf. p. 21 19c
E. M. Violette Museum, Kirks-

ville, Mo. cf. p. 17 19c
Museum of the Fur Trade,
Chadron, Nebr. cf. p. 17 19c
Valentine Museum, Richmond,
Va. cf. p. 21 18c; 19c
Moccasins - Seminole Indian Tribes:
House of Refuge Museum,
Stuart, Fla. cf. p. 15 19c
Dallas Historical Society, Dallas,
Texas cf. p. 21
Moccasins - Woodland Indians:
Museum of the American In-
dian, New York, N. Y. cf. p. 19
Overshoes: Rochester Museum of
Arts and Sciences, Rochester,
N. Y. cf. p. 19 18c
Shoes: E. M. Violette Museum,
Kirksville, Mo. cf. p. 17
900-1500 B. C.
Shoes-Button: E. M. Violette Mu-
seum, Kirksville, Mo. cf. p.
17 20c
Shoes-Dutch: Paramus Historical
and Preservation Society, Ridge-
wood, N. J. cf. p. 18 20c
Shoes-Gaiter:
Charles W. Bowers Memorial
Museum, Santa Ana, Calif.
cf. p. 14 19c
Valentine Museum, Richmond,
Va. cf. p. 21 18c
Shoes-Grass: Marine Historical
Association, Inc., Mystic, Conn.
cf. p. 14 19c
Shoes-Wooden: Marine Historical
Association, Inc., Mystic, Conn.
cf. p. 14 19c

Headdresses
Aigrettes-feathered plume head-
dress: Rochester Museum of
Arts and Sciences, Rochester,
N. Y. cf. p. 19 20c
Bonnets:
Charles W. Bowers Memorial
Museum, Santa Ana, Calif.
cf. p. 14 19c
Colebrook Historical Society,
Colebrook, Conn. cf. p. 14
19c
Marine Historical Association,
Inc., Mystic, Conn. cf. p. 14
19c

84

Nutley Historical Society Museum, Nutley, N.J. cf. p. 18 19c

Paramus Historical and Preservation Society, Ridgewood, N.J. cf. p. 18 19c

Rochester Museum of Arts and Sciences, Rochester, N.Y. cf. p. 19 19c

Rocky Ford Museum, Rocky Ford, Colo. cf. p. 14 19c

Stanton House, Clinton, Conn. cf. p. 14 19c

Swarthmore College Friends Historical Library, Swarthmore, Penna. cf. p. 20 19c

University of Rhode Island, Kingston, R.I. cf. p. 20 19c

Worcester Historical Society, Worcester, Mass. cf. p. 17 18c; 19c

Bonnets-Calash:

Charleston Museum, Charleston, S.C. cf. p. 21 18c

Colebrook Historical Society, Colebrook, Conn. cf. p. 14 19c; 20c

Danbury Scott-Fanton Museum and Historical Society, Inc., Danbury, Conn. cf. p. 14 18c; 19c

Hawaiian Mission Children's Society, Honolulu, Hawaii cf. p. 15 19c; 20c

Waterloo Library and Historical Society, Waterloo, N.Y. cf. p. 19 19c

Bonnets-Cover: Nassau County Historical Museum, East Meadow, L.I., N.Y. cf. p. 18 19c

Bonnets-Leghorn: Lancaster County Historical Society, Lancaster, Penna. cf. p. 20 19c

Bonnets-Silk:

Beyer Home, Oconto County Historical Museum, Oconto, Wisc. cf. p. 22 19c

Hood River County Historical Museum, Hood River, Oreg. cf. p. 20 19c

Bonnets-Straw: Lancaster County Historical Society, Lancaster, Penna. cf. p. 20 19c

Bonnets-Straw Poke: San Jacinto Monument and Museum, Houston, Texas cf. p. 21 19c

Bonnets-Sun: Valentine Museum, Richmond, Va. cf. p. 21 19c

Caps-Boudoir: Rochester Museum of Arts and Sciences, Rochester, N.Y. cf. p. 19 20c

Caps-Dust: Nassau County Historical Museum, East Meadow, L.I., N.Y. cf. p. 18 19c; 20c

Caps-Horned: Museum of the Fur Trade, Chadron, Nebr. cf. p. 17 19c

Caps-Night cap for men: Pipe Spring National Monument, Moccasin, Ariz. cf. p. 13 19c

Caps-Night cap for women: Rocky Ford Museum, Rocky Ford, Colo. cf. p. 14 19c

Caps-Sleeping: Nutley Historical Society Museum, Nutley, N.J. cf. p. 18 19c

Caps-Student's: Norwegian-American Historical Museum, Decorah, Iowa cf. p. 16 18c

Caplet-braid trimmed wool: Charles W. Bowers Memorial Museum, Santa Ana, Calif. cf. p. 14 19c

Hats-Beaver (men's or women's):

Beloit Historical Museum, Beloit, Wisc. cf. p. 21 19c

Camden County Historical Society, Camden, N.J. cf. p. 18 19c

Historical Museum of Wabash Valley, Terre Haute, Ind. cf. p. 15 19c; 20c

Historical Society of York County, York, Penna. cf. p. 20 19c

Marine Historical Association, Inc., Mystic, Conn. cf. p. 14 19c

Nassau County Historical Museum, East Meadow, L.I., N.Y. cf. p. 18 19c; 20c

Paramus Historical and Preservation Society, Ridgewood, N.J. cf. p. 18 19c

Pettigrew Museum, Sioux Falls, S.D. cf. p. 21 19c

Worcester Historical Society, Worcester, Mass. cf. p. 17

18c. 19c. 20c

Hats-Bowler: Nassau County Historical Museum, East Meadow, L. I. , N. Y. cf. p. 18 19c; 20c

Hats-Broad-brimmed plumed: Lancaster County Historical Society, Lancaster, Penna. cf. p. 20 19c

Hats-Cady: Beyer Home, Oconto County Historical Museum, Oconto, Wisc. cf. p. 22 19c

Hats-Chinese Mandarin: Marine Historical Association, Inc. Mystic, Conn. cf. p. 14 N

Hats-Cocked: Bostonian Society, Boston, Mass. cf. p. 16 19c

Hats-Coonskin fur: Tryon County Muzzle Loaders, Inc. , Fort Plain, N. Y. cf. p. 19 18c; 19c

Hats-Derby: Pipe Spring National Monument, Moccasin, Ariz. cf. p. 13 19c

Hats-Doctor's High hat: Oconto County Historical Museum, Oconto, Wisc. cf. p. 22 19c

Hats-Fur: Tryon County Muzzle Loaders, Inc. , Fort Plain, N. Y. cf. p. 19 18c; 19c

Hats-Indoor (Spanish): Charles W. Bowers Memorial Museum, Santa Ana, Calif. cf. p. 14 19c

Hats-Merry Widow: Beyer Home, Oconto County Historical Museum, Oconto, Wisc. cf. p. 22 19c

Hats-Mortar board (child's): Danbury Scott-Fanton Museum and Historical Society, Inc. , Danbury, Conn. cf. p. 14 19c

Hats-Mourning: Ossining Historical Society Museum, Ossining, N. Y. cf. p. 19 19c

Hats-Opera (men's):
Beyer Home, Oconto County Historical Museum, Oconto, Wisc. cf. p. 22 19c
Boulder Pioneer Museum, Boulder, Colo. cf. p. 14 19c; 20c

Pettigrew Museum, Sioux Falls, S. D. cf. p. 21 19c; 20c

Hats-Panama: Nassau County Historical Museum, East Meadow, L. I. , N. Y. cf. p. 18 19c; 20c

Hats-Riding: Mercer County Historical Society, Mercer, Penna. cf. p. 20 18c

Hats-Roaring 20's: Pettigrew Museum, Sioux Falls, S. D. cf. p. 21 20c

Hats-Sailor's:
Lancaster County Historical Society, Lancaster, Penna. cf. p. 20 19c
Marine Historical Association, Inc. , Mystic, Conn. cf. p. 14 19c

Hats-Silk:
Camden County Historical Society, Camden, N. J. cf. p. 18 19c
Colebrook Historical Society, Colebrook, Conn. cf. p. 14 19c
Nassau County Historical Museum, East Meadow, L. I. , N. Y. cf. p. 18 19c; 20c

Hats-Snood: San Jacinto Monument and Museum, Houston, Texas cf. p. 21 19c

Hats-Steeplecrown: Plymouth Antiquarian Society, Plymouth, Mass. cf. p. 17 17c

Hats-Stovepipe: Mercer County Historical Society, Mercer, Penna. cf. p. 20 18c

Hats-Tri-corn:
Camden County Historical Society, Camden, N. J. cf. p. 18 18c
Tryon County Muzzle Loaders, Inc. , Fort Plain, N. Y. cf. p. 19 18c; 19c
Worcester Historical Society, Worcester, Mass. cf. p. 17 18c; 19c

Hats-Top:
Clay County Historical Society, Moorhead, Minn. cf. p. 17 20c
Historical Museum of Wabash Valley, Terre Haute, Ind. cf. p. 15 19c; 20c
Nassau County Historical Mu-

seum, East Meadow, L. I.,
N. Y.   cf. p. 18   20c

Hats-Beaver: Marine Historical
Association, Inc., Mystic,
Conn.   cf. p. 14   19c

Hats-Gray velour: Boulder Pioneer Museum, Boulder, Colo.
cf. p. 14   20c

Hats-Rabbit: Porter-Phelps-
Huntington Historic House
Museum, Hadley, Mass.
cf. p. 16   19c

Hats-Silk: Boulder Pioneer Museum, Boulder, Colo.   cf.
p. 14   20c

Hats-Velvet (high, round, embroidered, beaded with 2"
band, tassel top): Charles
W. Bowers Memorial Mu-
seum, Santa Ana, Calif.
cf. p. 14   19c

Hats-Whaler's: Marine Historical Association, Inc.,
Mystic, Conn.   cf. p. 14
19c

Indian Headdress-Beaded In-
dian Hood:Museum of the
American Indian, New York,
N. Y.   cf. p. 19   N

Indian Headdress-Feathered
Indian Bonnet: Museum of
the American Indian, New
York, N. Y.   cf. p. 19   N

Indian Headdress-Medicine
Man's Headdress: Witte
Memorial Museum, San An-
tonio, Texas   cf. p. 21   N

Indian Headdress-Red-dyed
Deerhair Roach Headdress of
the Sioux tribe: Museum of
the Fur Trade, Chadron,
Nebr.   cf. p. 17   N

Indian Headdress-War Bonnet
of Sioux tribe with eagle
feathers: Museum of the Fur
Trade, Chadron, Nebr.   cf.
p. 17   N

Mantillas-Spanish: Charles W.
Bowers Memorial Museum,
Santa Ana, Calif.   cf. p. 14
19c

Shauts-Norwegian scarves: Norwegian-American Historical

Museum, Decorah, Iowa   cf.
p. 16   18c; 19c

Siam Silver and Crystal Head-
dresses and Epaulets: Witte
Memorial Museum, San Antonio,
Texas   cf. p. 21   N

Sombreros: Carnegie Museum,
Pittsburgh, Penna.   cf. p. 20
20c

Wigs: Valentine Museum, Richmond, Va.   cf. p. 21   18c

Lingerie

Corsets: Plymouth Antiquarian
Society, Plymouth, Mass.   cf.
p. 17   17c

Corset Couvers: Imperial County
Pioneer Museum, Imperial,
Calif.   cf. p. 13   19c

Pantalets:
Charles W. Bowers Memorial
Museum, Santa Ana, Calif.
cf. p. 14   19c
Marine Historical Association,
Inc., Mystic, Conn.   cf. p.
14   19c
Valentine Museum, Richmond,
Va.   cf. p. 21   19c

Men's Costumes

American Frontiersmen's costumes:
Tryon County Muzzle Loaders,
Inc., Fort Plain, N. Y.   cf.
p. 19   19c
Witte Memorial Museum, San
Antonio, Texas   cf. p. 21   19c

Breeches-Buckskin: Tryon County
Muzzle Loaders, Inc., Fort
Plain, N. Y.   cf. p. 19   18c

Breeches-Buff knee (breeches and
leggings): Danbury Scott-Fanton
Museum and Historical Society,
Inc., Danbury, Conn.   cf. p. 14
18c

Buckskin Clothing: Tryon County
Muzzle Loaders, Inc., Fort
Plain, N. Y.   cf. p. 19   18c

Ch'ing Dynasty Chinese costumes:
Witte Memorial Museum, San
Antonio, Texas   cf. p. 21   N

Cowboy's costume:
Dallas Historical Society, Dallas,
Texas   cf. p. 21   19c
Texas Memorial Museum, Austin,

Texas cf. p. 21 20c

Ghost-dance Skirt (buckskin):
Museum of the American
Indian, New York, N.Y.
cf. p. 19 N

Witte Memorial Museum,
San Antonio, Texas cf.
p. 21 N

Ice-cream Pants: Rochester
Museum of Arts and Sciences,
Rochester, N.Y. cf. p. 19
20c

Indian Chief's costume-Plains
Indian: Witte Memorial Museum, San Antonio, Texas
cf. p. 21 N

Merchant Costumes: Maryland
Historical Society, Baltimore,
Md. cf. p. 16 19c

Morning Shirt-Apache men's:
Witte Memorial Museum,
San Antonio, Texas cf.
p. 21 N

Motoring costumes: Museum of
Motoring Memories, Natural
Bridge, Va. cf. p. 21 20c

Planter's costume: Maryland
Historical Society, Baltimore, Md. cf. p. 16 19c

Tuxedos: Pettigrew Museum,
Sioux Falls, S.D. cf. p.
21 19c; 20c

Military
Armor: Dallas Historical Society, Dallas, Texas cf.
p. 21 18c

Armor-Battle Axes: John Woodman Higgins Armory, Inc.,
Worcester, Mass. cf. p.
17 16c; 17c

Armor-Breast Plates: George
F. Harding Museum, Chicago,
Ill. cf. p. 15 900-1500 B.C.

Armor-Chanfrons: George F.
Harding Museum, Chicago,
Ill. cf. p. 15 900-1500 B.C.

Armor-Crossbows: John
Woodman Higgins Armory,
Inc., Worcester, Mass.
cf. p. 17 16c; 17c

Armor-Daggers: John Wood-
man Higgins Armory, Inc.,

Worcester, Mass. cf. p. 17
16c; 17c

Armor-Gauntlets: George F.
Harding Museum, Chicago, Ill.
cf. p. 15 900-1500 B.C.

Armor-Hand Cannon: John Woodman Higgins Armory, Inc.,
Worcester, Mass. cf. p. 17
16c; 17c

Armor-Hand Gun: John Woodman
Higgins Armory, Inc., Worcester,
Mass. cf. p. 17 16c; 17c

Armor-Lances: John Woodman
Higgins Armory, Inc., Worcester,
Mass. cf. p. 17 16c; 17c

Armor-Maces: John Woodman
Higgins Armory, Inc., Worcester,
Mass. cf. p. 17 16c; 17c

Armor-Pole Arms: John Woodman
Higgins Armory, Inc., Worcester,
Mass. cf. p. 17 16c; 17c

Armor-Shields: John Woodman
Higgins Armory, Inc., Worcester,
Mass. cf. p. 17 16c; 17c

Armor-Spurs: John Woodman
Higgins Armory, Inc., Worcester,
Mass. cf. p. 17 16c; 17c

Armor-Stirrups: John Woodman
Higgins Armory, Inc., Worcester,
Mass. cf. p. 17 16c; 17c

Armor-Swords: John Woodman
Higgins Armory, Inc., Worcester,
Mass. cf. p. 17 16c; 17c

Brahman Caste costumes-East
Indian: Witte Memorial Museum,
San Antonio, Texas cf. p. 21 N

Confederate Officer's uniform:
Historic Mobile Preservation Society, Mobile, Ala. cf. p. 13 19c

Epaulets: Dallas Historical Society,
Dallas, Texas cf. p. 21 19c

Epaulets-Colonel's: Danbury Scott-
Fanton Museum and Historical
Society, Inc., Danbury, Conn.
cf. p. 14 19c

Epaulets-Navy. from the Civil and
Spanish-American Wars: Marine
Historical Association, Inc.,
Mystic, Conn. cf. p. 14 19c

Helmets-Armet: George F. Harding Museum, Chicago, Ill. cf.
p. 15 900-1500 B.C.

Helmets-Barbute: George F.
Harding Museum, Chicago,
Ill. cf. p.15 900-1500
B.C.
Helmets-Burgonet: George F.
Harding Museum, Chicago,
Ill. cf. p.15 900-1500
B.C.
Helmets-Cabasset: George F.
Harding Museum, Chicago,
Ill. cf. p.15 900-1500
B.C.
Helmets-Casque: George F.
Harding Museum, Chicago,
Ill. cf. p.15 900-1500
B.C.
Helmets-Death Head: George
F. Harding Museum, Chicago,
Ill. cf. p.15 900-1500 B.C.
Helmets-Doughboy: Beyer
Home, Oconto County His-
torical Museum, Oconto,
Wisc. cf. p.22 20c
Helmets-French: M.H.De
Young Memorial Museum,
San Francisco, Calif. cf.
p.14 19c
Helmets-German: M.H.De
Young Memorial Museum,
San Francisco, Calif. cf.
p.14 19c
Helmets-Morion: George F.
Harding Museum, Chicago,
Ill. cf. p.15 900-1500
B.C.
Helmets-Mortuary: George F.
Harding Museum, Chicago,
Ill. cf. p.15 900-1500
B.C.
Helmets-Pig's Nose: George
F. Harding Museum, Chicago,
Ill. cf. p.15 900-1500 B.C.
Helmets-Salade: George F.
Harding Museum, Chicago,
Ill. cf. p.15 900-1500 B.C.
Hussars Uniforms of 1810:
Bostonian Society, Boston,
Mass. cf. p.16 19c
Jousting costumes: John Wood-
man Higgins Armory, Inc.
Worcester, Mass. cf. p.
17 16c; 17c
Samurai Suit of Armor: Witte

Memorial Museum, San Antonio,
Texas cf. p.21 N
State Guards Uniforms: State Museum, Denver, Colo. cf. p.
14 19c
Zouave French Infantry Uniform:
Nassau County Historical Museum, East Meadow, L.I., N.Y.
cf. p.18 19c

Neckwear
Boas-fur neckpieces: Valentine
Museum, Richmond, Va. cf.
p.21 19c
Cravats-neckwear for men:
Rochester Museum of Arts and
Sciences, Rochester, N.Y.
cf. p.19 19c
Valentine Museum, Richmond,
Va. cf. p.21 19c
Dickey-insertions for the neck
(either sex): Pipe Spring National
Monument, Moccasin, Ariz.
cf. p.13 19c
Fichus-neckwear for women:
Rocky Ford Museum, Rocky
Ford, Colo. cf. p.14 19c
Jabots-neckpiece for men:
Pipe Spring National Monument,
Moccasin, Ariz. cf. p.13
19c
Valentine Museum, Richmond,
Va. cf. p.21 19c

Organizational Costumes
Campfire Girls Uniforms: Rochester
Museum of Arts and Sciences,
Rochester, N.Y. cf. p.19 20c
Fraternal Lodge Uniforms: State
Museum, Denver, Colo. cf.
p.14 19c
Girl Scout Uniforms: Rochester
Museum of Arts and Sciences,
Rochester, N.Y. cf. p.19 20c
Ku Klux Klan costumes: State
Museum, Denver, Colo. cf.
p.14 19c. 20c

Over Garments
Automobile dusters with accessories:
Rochester Museum of Arts and
Sciences, Rochester, N.Y. cf.
p.19 20c
Capes-Naval Victorian: Marine

New York, N. Y. cf. p. 19 N

Painted Caribou-skin Indian Coat: Museum of the American Indian, New York, N. Y. cf. p. 19 N

Robes-Baptismal: Garrett County Historical Society, Oakland, Md. cf. p. 16 19c

Robes-Borning: Sharlot Hall, Prescott, Ariz. cf. p. 13 19c

Robes-Christening: City Art Museum of St. Louis, St. Louis, Mo. cf. p. 17 19c

Robes-Dragon (Chinese embroidered): Montclair Art Museum, Montclair, N. J. cf. p. 18 19c

Robes-Lounging: Valentine Museum, Richmond, Va. cf. p. 21 18c

Robes-Lutheran Pulpit: North Dakota Institute, Fargo, N. D. cf. p. 19 19c

Robes-Mandarin (Japanese): Marine Historical Association, Inc., Mystic, Conn. cf. p. 14 19c

Robes-Maternity: Valentine Museum, Richmond, Va. cf. p. 21 19c

Robes-Red "Kashmir": Montclair Art Museum, Montclair, N. J. cf. p. 18 18c

Robes-Smoking: Valentine Museum, Richmond, Va. cf. p. 21 18c

Professional

Academic Robes: Beyer Home, Oconto County Historical Museum, Oconto, Wisc. cf. p. 22 20c

Boxer's Chinese Male Dress costume: Oakland Public Museum, Oakland, Calif. cf. p. 14 19c

Circus costumes: Ringling Circus Museum, Sarasota, Fla. cf. p. 15 19c

College Girls Uniforms by Peter Thompson: Rochester Museum of Arts and Sciences, Rochester, N. Y. cf. p. 19 20c

Jockey Jackets: Charleston Museum, Charleston, S. C. cf. p. 21 19c; 20c

Maid's costume: Rochester Museum of Arts and Sciences, Rochester, N. Y. cf. p. 19 20c

Medicine Man's costume-Seminole Indian tribe: House of Refuge Museum, Stuart, Fla. cf. p. 15 19c

Nurses Uniforms: Museum of History and Industry, Seattle, Wash. cf. p. 21 19c

Red Cross Uniforms:
Nutley Historical Society Museum, Nutley, N. J. cf. p. 18 19c
Rochester Museum of Arts and Sciences, Rochester, N. Y. cf. p. 19 20c

Sporting Costumes

Baseball Uniforms of U. S. A.: National Baseball Hall of Fame and Museum, Cooperstown, N. Y. cf. p. 18 19c; 20c

Bathing Suits (women's):
Rochester Museum of Arts and Sciences, Rochester, N. Y. cf. p. 19 19c
Valentine Museum, Richmond, Va. cf. p. 21 19c

Golf Knickers: Rochester Museum of Arts and Sciences, Rochester, N. Y. cf. p. 19 20c

Hunting Suit and Game Bag: Rochester Museum of Arts and Sciences, Rochester, N. Y. cf. p. 19 20c

Riding Habits-Men's: Charleston Museum, Charleston, S. C. cf. p. 21 20c

Riding Habits-Women's:
Detroit Historical Society, Detroit, Mich. cf. p. 17 19c
Rochester Museum of Arts and Sciences, Rochester, N. Y. cf. p. 19 19c

Valentine Museum, Richmond, Va. cf. p. 21 19c

Women's Costumes

Baluchar Sari-Western Bengal: Witte Memorial Museum, San Antonio, Texas cf. p. 21 N

Basque:
Rocky Ford Museum, Rocky Ford, Colo. cf. p. 14 19c
San Jacinto Monument and Museum, Houston, Texas cf. p. 21 19c

Batik and Tapa Cloth-used as wrap-arounds by natives of Malay: Historical Museum of Wabash Valley, Terre Haute, Ind. cf. p. 15 19c; 20c

Beaded Indian Dress: Museum of the American Indian, New York, N. Y. cf. p. 19 N

Best Gowns: Worcester Historical Society, Worcester, Mass. cf. p. 17 19c

Brittany-national costume: Montclair Art Museum, Montclair, N. J. cf. p. 18 20c

Buckskin dress-Apache: Museum of Navajo Ceremonial Art, Santa Fe, N. Mex. cf. p. 18 19c

Bustle dress: Ossining Historical Society Museum, Ossining, N. Y. cf. p. 19 19c

Calico dresses:
Ossining Historical Society Museum, Ossining, N. Y. cf. p. 19 19c
Tryon County Muzzle Loaders, Inc., Fort Plain, N. Y. cf. p. 19 18c

Chemise Dress: Imperial County Pioneer Museum, Imperial, Calif. cf. p. 13 19c

Dolman Dress: Beloit Historical Museum, Beloit,

Wisc. cf. p. 21 19c

Dressing Gowns:
Henry Francis du Pont Winterthur Museum, Winterthur, Del. cf. p. 14 19c
Sleepy Hollow Restorations, Tarrytown, N. Y. cf. p. 19 18c

Dress-Up: Carnegie Museum, Pittsburgh, Penna. cf. p. 20 19c

Empire Styled Dress: Ossining Historical Society Museum, Ossining, N. Y. cf. p. 19 19c

Eskimo Sealskin Costume: Museum of the American Indian, New York, N. Y. cf. p. 19 N

Funeral Dress: Montgomery Museum of Fine Arts, Montgomery, Ala. cf. p. 13 19c

Gay Nineties Dresses: New Haven Colony Historical Society, New Haven, Conn. cf. p. 14 19c

Going-Away Dress: Mercer County Historical Society, Mercer, Penna. cf. p. 20 18c

Grass-Skirts-Northwestern Pacific Indian Tribe: Ponco City Indian Museum, Ponco City, Okla. cf. p. 20 20c

Inaugural Gowns: Cole County Historical Society, Jefferson City, Mo. cf. p. 17 U

Java-Batik Sarong: Montclair Art Museum, Montclair, N. J. cf. p. 18 19c

Kimonos-Chinese and Japanese: Charles W. Bowers Memorial Museum, Santa Ana, Calif. cf. p. 14 19c

Mother Hubbard Costume: Oconto County Historical Museum, Oconto, Wisc. cf. p. 22 19c

Mourning Dress:
Ossining Historical Society Museum, Ossining, N. Y. cf. p. 19 19c
Valentine Museum, Richmond, Va. cf. p. 21 19c

Mull Dress: Ossining Historical Society Museum, Ossining, N. Y. cf. p. 19 19c

Pannier-in a rust brocade and

satin: Howard County Historical Society, Kokomo, Ind. cf. p. 15   19c

Roaring 20's Dresses: Pettigrew Museum, Sioux Falls, S. D. cf. p. 21   20c

Robes de chambre-morning gown: Rochester Museum of Arts and Sciences, Rochester, N. Y. cf. p. 19   20c

Sacque Dresses: Valentine Museum, Richmond, Va. cf. p. 21   19c; 20c

Sarongs-Java-Batik: Montclair Art Museum, Montclair, N. J. cf. p. 18   19c

Sarongs-Siam: Witte Memorial Museum, San Antonio, Texas cf. p. 21   N

Shirt Waists: Rochester Museum of Arts and Sciences, Rochester, N. Y. cf. p. 19   19c; 20c

Tea Gowns: Rochester Museum of Arts and Sciences, Rochester, N. Y. cf. p. 19   19c

Tyrolian Costumes-Austrian: Montclair Art Museum, Montclair, N. J. cf. p. 18   N

Wedding Gowns:
  Boulder Pioneer Museum, Boulder, Colo. cf. p. 14   20c
  Marine Historical Association, Inc., Mystic, Conn. cf. p. 14   19c
  North Dakota Institute, Fargo, N. D. cf. p. 19   19c
  Norwegian-American Historical Museum, Decorah, Iowa cf. p. 16   19c
  Paramus Historical and Preservation Society, Ridgewood, N. J. cf. p. 18   19c
  Pettigrew Museum, Sioux Falls, S. D. cf. p. 21   20c

Rochester Museum of Arts and Sciences, Rochester, N. Y. cf. p. 19   19c

Rocky Ford Museum, Rocky Ford, Colo. cf. p. 14   19c

San Jacinto Monument and Museum, Houston, Texas cf. p. 21   19c

Sharlot Hall Historical Museum of Arizona, Prescott, Ariz. cf. p. 13   19c

Sheldon Swope Art Gallery, Terre Haute, Ind. cf. p. 15   19c

Wedding Costumes-
  Chinese Wedding Costumes: Seattle Art Museum, Seattle, Wash. cf. p. 21   N
  Japanese Wedding Kimono: Witte Memorial Museum, San Antonio, Texas cf. p. 21   N
  Norwegian Hardanger: Norwegian-American Historical Museum, Decorah, Iowa cf. p. 16   N

Widow's Weeds-women's evening gowns: Rochester Museum of Arts and Sciences, Rochester, N. Y. cf. p. 19   19c

Wrapper: Valentine Museum, Richmond, Va. cf. p. 21   19c

PART TWO

Europe

Institutions

by

Country

Institutions by Country - Europe

Austria

Bregenz
Vorarlberger Landesmuseum, Kornmarkt I

Eisenstadt
Burgenländisches Landesmuseum, Meierhofgasse 157

Graz
Steirisches Völkskundemuseum, Paulustorgasse Nr. 13, Steiermark

Innsbruck
Tiroler Völkskunstmuseum (Tyrolese Peasant's Museum), Universitätsstrasse, 2

Klagenfurt
Kärntner Landesmuseum, Museumgasse 2

Linz
Öberosterreichisches Landesmuseum, Museumgasse 14

Salsburg
Völkskundliche Sammlung des Salzburger Museums

Vienna
Die Kostümausstellung im K. K. Österreichischen Museum

Dom- und Diözesanmuseum (Episcopal Museum), Rothenturmstrasse 2

Erstes Österreichisches Heimatmuseum für den Böhmerwald, und das Erzgebirge, Czapkagasse 16/I/6

Geistliche und Weltliche Schatzkammer (Secular and Ecclesiastical Treasury), Schweizerhof, Saulenstiege

Heeresgeschichtliches Museum, (Austrian Army Museum), Arsenal

Heimatmuseum, f. d. Böhmerwald u. d. Erzgebirge, Czapkagasse 16, Büro

Historisches Museum der Stadt Wien (Historical Museum of the City of Vienna), Modesammlungen (Fashion Collection), Hetzendorfer Strasse 79, Schloss Hetzendorf

Kostüm-Sammlung der Akademie der bildenden Künste, Schillerplatz 3

Kunsthistorisches Museum (Museum of Fine Arts), Neue Hofburg, Heldenplatz

Niederösterreichisches Landesmuseum (Museum of the Province of Lower Austria), Herrengasse 9

Österreichisches Museum für angewandte Kunst (Austrian Museum of Applied Art), Stubenring 5

Österreichisches Museum für Völkskunde (The Austrian Folklore Museum), Laudongasse 15-19

Schlesisches Heimatmuseum und viele weitere Heimatmuseen

Vorarlberg
Heimatmuseum Egg, Trachtensammlung

Belgium

Brussels
Musée Royaux d'Armes et d'Armures (Museum of Royal Arms and Armours), Porte de Hal

Musée Royaux d'Art et
d'Histoire, 10 Parc du
Cinquantenaire

British Isles
Ireland

Dublin
Ard-Mhúsaem Na h-Éireann
(National Museum of Ireland),
Kildare Street

Genealogical Office, (Office
of Arms), Dublin Castle

British Isles
United Kingdom
England

Abingdon
Borough Museum Collections,
The County Hall, Bershire
Aldershot
Army School of Physical
Training Museum, Queen's
Avenue, Hampshire
Alton
Curtis Museum, High
Street, Hampshire
Aylesbury
Bucks County Museum, Church
Street, Buckinghamshire
Barnard Castle
Bowes Museum,
Durham
Basingstoke
Willis Museum, New
Street, Hampshire
Bath
Museum of Costume, Somer-
set
Bignor
Bignor Roman Villa Collec-
tion, Sussex
Birmingham
Birmingham City Museum and
Art Gallery, The Departments
of Archaeology, Ethnography,
and Birmingham History,
Congreve Street
Bletchley
Woburn Abbey, Buckinghamshire
Blithfield
Museum of Childhood and

Costume, Blithfield Hall, Nr.
Rugeley, Staffordshire
Bradford 4
Bradford City Art Gallery and
Museums, Bolling Hall
Museum, Yorkshire
Bristol
Blaize Castle Museum
Burnley
Gawthorpe Hall, Lancashire
Camberley
National Army Museum,
R. M. A. Sandhurst (War
Office), Surrey
Cambridge
Scott Polar Research Institute,
Lensfield Road,
Cambridgeshire
Canterbury
Westgate, Kent
Carlisle
The Castle, The Border Regiment
The Keep, Cumberland
Chelmsford
Chelmsford and Essex Muse-
um, Oaklands Park, Essex
Cheltenham
Cheltenham Art Gallery and
Museum, Clarence Street,
Gloucestershire
Christchurch
Red House Museum and Art
Gallery, Quay Road, Hants
Deal
Deal Museum, Town Hall,
High Street, Kent
Dorchester
Dorset Military Museum,
The Keep, Dorset
Farleigh-Hungerford
Farleigh Castle Museum,
Somerset
Gainsborough
Gainsborough Old Hall,
Parnell Street, Lincolnshire
Guernsey
Guille Alles Museum, St.
Peter Port, Channel Islands
Guildford
Albury Park House, Surrey

Eridge Castle Costume Mu-
seum, Surrey

Halifax
  Bankfield Museum and Art
  Gallery, Akroyd Park, York-
  shire
Hatfield
  Hatfield House, Hertfordshire
Hereford
  Hereford City Museum and
  Art Gallery, Broad Street,
  Herefordshire

  Herefordshire Light Infantry
  Regimental Museum, Harold
  Street, Herefordshire
Hove
  Hove Museum of Art, New
  Church Road, Sussex
Hull
  Londesborough Barracks, 4th.
  BN. The East Yorkshire
  Regiment, Yorkshire
Ipswich
  Christchurch Mansion, Christ-
  church Park, Suffolk

  Ipswich Museum, High Street,
  Suffolk
Jersey
  Gorey Castle Museum, Gorey
  District, Channel Islands
Kettering
  Westfield Museum, West
  Street, Northamptonshire
Lancaster
  King's Own Regimental Mu-
  seum, Old Town Hall,
  Market Square, Lancashire
Leeds
  Abbey House Museum, Kirk-
  stall, Yorkshire

  Temple Newsam House,
  Yorkshire
Leicester
  Newarke House, The, Branch
  Museum, Leicestershire
Lewes
  Anne of Cleaves House, High
  Street, Southover, Sussex
Lichfield
  Lichfield Art Gallery and Mu-
  seum, Museum Buildings,
  Bird Street, Staffordshire
Lincoln

Lincoln City and County Museum, Broadgate, Lincoln

Lingfield
  Women's Royal Army Corps,
  Depot and Training Center,
  Regimental Museum, Hobbs
  Barracks, Surrey
Liverpool
  Sudley Art Gallery and Mu-
  seum, Mossley Hill Road,
  Lancashire
London
  Armouries (The Tower of
  London)

  Bethnal Green Museum,
  Cambridge Heath Road

  British Museum, Great Russell
  Street and Southampton Row

  Dickens House, 48
  Doughty Street

  Guildhall Museum, The Royal
  Exchange

  Imperial War Museum,
  Lambeth Road

  London Irish Rifles Museum,
  Duke of York's Headquarters,
  Sloane Square

  London Museum, Kensington
  Road

  National Maritime Museum,
  Greenwich

  Royal Fusiliers, Tower
  of London, Tower Hill

  Tower of London, Key K 4

  Victoria and Albert Museum,
  South Kensington

  Wallace Collection,
  Baker Street, Manchester
  Square

  Wellington Museum, Apsley
  House, Hyde Park Corner

  Westminster Abbey
Ludlow
  Ludlow Museum, Butter Cross,
  Shropshire

Luton
   Luton Museum and Art Gallery,
   Wardown Park, Bedfordshire
Manchester
   Gallery of English
   Costume, Platt Hall
Newcastle-upon-Tyne
   Laing Art Gallery and Muse-
   um, Regimental Museum,
   Fenham Barracks
Northampton
   Central Museum and Art
   Gallery, Guildhall Road,
   Northamptonshire
Nottingham
   Nottingham City Museum and
   Art Gallery, The Castle,
   Nottinghamshire
Pontefract
   Castle Museum, Ponte-
   fract Castle, Yorkshire
Preston
   Harris Museum and Art
   Gallery, Market Square,
   Lancashire
Rotherham
   Rotherham Museum and Art
   Gallery, Clifton Park,
   Yorkshire
Salisbury
   Salisbury, South Wilts and
   Blackmore Museum, St. Ann
   Street, Wiltshire
Stockton-on-Tees
   Preston Hall Museum and Art
   Gallery, Preston Park,
   Eaglescliffe, Durham
Stow-on-the-Wold
   St. Edward's Hall Museum,
   Gloucestershire
Tonbridge
   Penhurst Place, Kent
Totnes
   Elizabethan House, 70
   Fore Street, Devon
Wakefield
   City Museum, Mechanics
   Institute, Wood Street,
   Yorkshire
Warwick
   St. John's House, Coten End,
   Warwickshire

Warwick Castle Museum,
Warwickshire
Worthing
   Worthing Museum and Art
   Gallery, Chapel Road, Sussex
York
   Castle Museum, Costume
   and Military Sections,
   Debtor's Prison, Yorkshire

   Railway Museum, Queen
   Street, Small Exhibits Section,
   Yorkshire

         Northern Ireland
Armagh
   Armagh County Museum, The
   Mall
Belfast
   Ulster Museum, Stranmillis
   Road 9, Antrim

         Scotland
Blair Atholl
   Blair Castle and Atholl Mu-
   seum, Perth
Dunfermline
   Pittencrieff House Museum,
   Pittencrieff Park, Fife
Edinburgh
   Annex: The Museum Gallery,
   18 Shandwick Place (West
   end of Princes Street)

   Canongate Tolbooth Museum,
   Royal Mile

   Collection of J. Telfer Dunbar, Lady Stair's House,
   Lady Stair's Close, Lawn
   market

   Huntley House Museum, Royal
   Mile

   Museum of Childhood, Hynd-
   ford's Close, 34 High Street

   National Museum of
   Antiquities of Scotland, Queen
   Street

   Scottish United Services Museum, Crown Square,
   Edinburgh Castle

Glamis
  Angus Folk Collection,
  Kirkwynd, Angus
Glasgow
  City of Glasgow Corporation
  Art Gallery and Museum,
  Kelvingrove
Kingussie
  Highland Folk Museum,
  Inverness
Paisley
  Paisley Museum and Art
  Galleries, High Street, Renfrew

Wales
Abergavenny
  Abergavenny and District
  Museum, Castle House,
  Monmouth
Bangor
  Museum of Welsh Antiquities,
  University College of North
  Wales, College Road,
  Caernarvon
Caernarvon
  Royal Welch Fusiliers,
  Queen's Tower
Cardiff
  Welsh Folk Museum, St.
  Fagans Castle
Carmarthen
  County Museum,
Llandudno
  Rapallo House Museum and
  Art Gallery, Fferm Bach
  Craig-y-Don, Caernarvon

Bulgaria
Sofia
  Ethnographisches Museum,
  Moskowska Str. 6a

Denmark
Copenhagen (København)
  Arsenal Museum (Tøjhuset)
  3 Tøjhusgade

  The National Museum,
  Frederiksholms Kanal

  Rosenborg Castle

  Skive (Dänemark) Museum

France
Agde
  Musée Agathois, Rue de la
  Fraternité, Hérault
Agen
  Musée Municipal, Place de
  l'Hôtel-de-Ville, Lot-et-
  Garonne
Alençon
  Musée de la Maison d'Oźe
  Place de la Magdeleine, Orne
Apt
  Chapelle Royale de Sainte-
  Anne (Cathedral of Saint
  Anne), Vaucluse
Bayonne
  Musée Basses-Pyrenees
Beaugency
  Musée Dunois, Château of the
  Sires of Beaugency, Loiret
Beaune
  Hôtel-Dieu Museum, rue de
  l'Hôtel-Dieu, Burgandy
Bourges
  (Musée du Berry), Hôtel Cujas
  4 and 6 rue   des Arenes,
  Cher
Carnac
  Musée Préhistorique, J. Miln
  - Z. le Rouzic, Morbihan
Chartres
  Musée Municipal, 29 Cloitre
  Notre-Dame, Eure-et-Loir
Château-Gombert
  Musée Local de l'Art
  Provencal (Museum of
  Provincial Art), 5   Place des
  Heros, Marseille
Clermont-Ferrand
  Musée des Beaux-Arts (Musée
  Bargoin), 45   rue de
  Ballainvilliers, Puy-de Dome

  Musée Historique, 34   rue
  des Gras, Puy-de-Dôme
Colmar
  Musée Unterlinden, 1   Place
  d'Unterlinden, Haut-Rhin
Corsica
  Permanent Exhibition of
  Corsican Costumes, 5   rue
  du Maréchal-Orvano

Croix-de-Vie
Musée Maraichin, Vendée

Dijon
Musée des Beaux-Arts, Place
de la Sainte-Chapelle, Côte-
d'Or

Musée Perrin de Puycousin,
40 rue des Forges at Dijon,
Côte-d'Or

Épernay
Musée du Vin de Champagne,
Château Pérrier, 13 Avenue
de Champagne, Marne

Fontainebleau
Musée Militaire, 15 rue
Royale, Seine-et-Marne

Gap
Musée des Hautes-Alpes, 4
Avenue d'Embrun, Hautes-
Alpes

Grasse
Musée Fragonard, 2 Passage
Mirabeau, Alpes-Maritimes

Honfleur
Musée des Beaux-Arts, rue
Albert Ist, Calvados

Musée Normand d'Ethnographie
et d'Art Populaire du Vieux-
Honfleur, Quai Saint-Etienne,
Calvados

La Chatre
Musée de la Vallée Noire,
71 rue Venôse, Indre

Le Mans
Musée des Beaux-Arts
(Musée de Tessé), rue de
Tessé, Sarthe

Le Puy-en-Velay
Musée Crozatier, Vinay
Gardens, Haute-Loire

Les Eyzies
Musée de Préhistoire,
Dordogne

Lille
Musée Industriel et Agricole,
Avenue du Peuple-Belge, Nord

Limoges
Musée Municipal de L'Evêché,
Place de la Cathédrals,
Haute-Vienne

Lourdes
Musée Pyrénéen, Old Castle,

Hautes-Pyrenees

Lyon
Musée Historique des Tissus,
34 rue de la Charité

Musée Lyonnais des Arts
Décoratifs, 30 rue de la
Charité, Rhone

Mâcon
Musée des Beaux-Arts, Quai
Lamartine, Saône-et-Loire

Mulhouse
Musée Historique, 4 Place
Guillaume-Tell, Haut-Rhin

Nancy
Musée Historique Lorrain,
Grand-rue, Meurthe-et-
Moselle

Nantes
Musée des Arts Décoratifs
et d'Art Populaire Régional,
Loire-Inférieure

Nice
Musée Masséna, 65 rue de
France and 35, Promenade
des Anglais, Alpes-Maritimes

Niort
Musée du Donjon, Deaux-
Sévres

Obernai
Musée Historique, Hôtel de
Ville, Bas-Rhin

Paris
Bibliothèque Nationale, Cabinet
des Médailles et des Antiques,
58 rue de Richelieu

Musée de l'Armée (Museum
of the Army), Hôtel des
Invalides, Paris 7e

Musée des Arts Décoratifs,
107 rue de Rivoli

Musée des Arts et Traditions
Populaires, Palais de
Chaillot, Place du Trocadéro,
Paris XVIe

Musée Carnavalet, 23 rue
de Sévigné, Paris IIIe

Musée de Cluny (Museum of
Cluny), 24 rue du Sommerard

Musée du Costume de la ville
de Paris, 11 Avenue du

Presidént Wilson, Paris XVI

Musée de l'Homme, Muséum
National D'Histoire Naturelle,
Palais de Chaillot

Musée de la Marine, Palais
de Chaillot

Musée de la Préfecture de
Police, 36 Quai des Orfèvres

Musée de l'Histoire de France,
60 rue des Francs-Bourgeois

Musée du Louvre, Palais du
Louvre, Porte Denon, Place
du Carrousel

Musée du Vieux-Montmartre,
17 rue Saint-Vincent

Pau
Musée Régional Béarnais, 3
Etage du Château de Pau,
Basses-Pyrénées

Péronne
Musée Danicourt, Somme

Pont-l'Abbé
Musée Bigouden, Finistère

Quimper
Musée Départmental Breton,
Rue du Roi-Gradlon, Finistere

Rennes
Archives Départementales d'
Ille-et-Vilaine, 2 Place S.-
Melaine, Ille-et-Vilaine

Musée de Bretagne, 20 Quai
Émile-Zola, Ille-et-Vilaine

Reims
Musée du Vieux Reims, 36
Place du Forum, Marne

Saint-Amarin
Musée Serret et de la Vallée
de Saint-Amarin, Haut-Rhin

Saint-Bertrand-de-Comminges
Cathedral, Haute-Garonne

Saint-German-en-Laye
Musée des Antiquités
Nationales, Seine-et-Oise

Saint-Malo
Quic-en-Groigne Gallery,
Château de Saint-Malo,
Ille-et-Vilaine

Sarrebourg
Musée Régional, Moselle

Senlis
Musée de la Vénerie, Royal
Château-Priory of Saint-
Maurice, Oise

Sens
Cathedral of Saint-Stephen,
Place de la République, Yonne

Sète
Musée Municipal
Place Stalingrad, Hérault

Strasbourg
Musée Alsaçien, 23 quai St.
Nicolas, Bas-Rhin

Abbe 'de Murbach

Musée de l'Oeuvre Notre-
Dame, 3 Place du Château

Musée Historique, Pont du
Corbeau, Bas-Rhin

Thiers
Musée Fontenille-Mondiére,
6 rue de Barente, Puy-de-
Dôme

Toulouse
Musée Paul Dupuy, 13 rue
de la Plau, Haute-Garonne

Musée Saint-Raymond, Place
Saint-Sernin, Haute-Garonne

Tourcoing
Musée des Tissus d'Art et
du Costume Ancien (Museum
of Ancient Costumes), Chamber
of Commerce, Nord

Tournus
Musée Bourguignon Perrin de
Puycousin (Museum of
Burgundy), 8 Place de Abbaye,
Saône-et-Loire

Troyes
Musée des Beaux-Arts, 21
rue Chrétien-de-Troyes Aube

Verdun
Musée de la Princerie, 16
rue de la Belle-Vierge, Meuse

Germany

Berlin
Kaiser-Friedrich Museum

Museum für Völkerkunde,
Arnimallee 23

Celle

103

Bomann-Museum Celle,
Schlosspaltz 7
Dresden
Historisches Museum (History
Museum), A-1 Zwinger

Erbach/Odenwald
Graflich Erbach-Erbach und
Wartenberg-Rothifche
Rentkammer, Der Rittersaal
(Knight's Hall), Postfach Nr.
27
Frankfurt am Main
Historisches Museum und
Munzkabinett, Saalgasse 31
Hamburg
Museum für Hamburgische
Geschichte, Holstenwall 24

Museum für Kunst und
Gewerbe

Museum für Völkerkunde und
Vorgeschichte
Hannover
Niedersächsische Landesgalerie
Kassel
Hessiches Landesmuseum
Leihgestern
Hüttenberger Heimatmuseum,
Rathausstraat
Lüdenscheid
Museum der Stadt Lüdenscheid,
Liebigstraat 11
Mainz
Catheral Museum
Munich
Bayerisches Nationalmuseum
(Bayer. National Museum),
Prinzregentenstrasse 3

Kostümforschungs
Institut, Kemnatenstraat 50
Nürnberg
National Museum
Schleswig
Landesmuseum für Vor- und
Fruhgeschichte von Schleswig-
Holstein, Schloss Gottorp
Speyer
Historisches Museum der
Pfalz mit Weinmuseum
(History Museum of Pfalz),
Gr. Pfaffengasse 7

Stendal
Heimatmuseum

Greece
Rhodes
Archaeological Institut

Hungary
Budapest
Kungstgew.-Museum

Nationalmuseum

Italy
Florence
Museo Nazionale, (Hall of
Arms)

Museum of Precious Stones

Museo Stibbert, Via
Vittorio Emanuele
Milan
Museo di Milano, Via S
Andrea 6

Museo della Baslica di S.
Ambrogio

Museo del Risorgimento,
Palazzo de Marchi, Via
Borgonuovo 23

Museo Navali, Via S. Vittore,
21
Naples
Museo Filangieri, Via
Duomo 288

Museo Nazionale di Capodi-
monte (Capodimonte National
Museum and Galleries),
Farnese Armory, Palazzo di
Capodimonte (Royal Palace
at Capodimonte)
Perugia
Galleria dell'Umbria, Palazzo
dei Priori
Rieti
Museo Civico (Civic Museum)
Rome
Monumenti Musei e Gallerie
Pontificie (The Vatican Art
Museum and Galleries), Citta
del Vaticano

104

Museo Sacro de
Biblioteca Vaticano
Turin
Armeria Reale (The Royal
Armoury), Piazza Castello,
191
Venice
Ca'Rezzonico, S. Marco 52

Museo Correr (Correr Museum), S. Marco 52

Museo del Risorgimento, S.
Marco 52

Museo Storico Navale

The Netherlands
Amsterdam
Nederlandsch Historisch
Scheepvaart Museum (The
Netherlands Museum of
Shipping History), Cornelis
Schuytsraat 57

Rijksmuseum (The Netherlands National Gallery),
Stadhouderskade 42
Arnhem
Rijksmuseum voor Völkskunde,
"Het Nederlands Openlucht-
museum" (The Netherlands
Open Air Museum),
Schelmseweg 89
Deventer
Museum de Waag, Brink 56
Dordrecht
Museum Simon van Giijn
Enkhuizen
Rijksmuseum Zuiderzee-
museum, Wierdijk 13
Groningen
Groningen Museum voor Stad
en Lande (Municipal and
Provincial Museum),
Praediniussingel 59
The Hague
Musée Postal Neerlandais
(The Netherlands Postal
Museum), Zeestraat 82

Nederlands Kostuummuseum
(The Netherlands Costume
Museum), Kabinet van Mode
en Smaak, Lange Vüjverberg
14

s'-Hertogenbosch
Central North Brabant Museum, Bethaniëstraat 4
Hindeloopen
Gemeentemuseum de Hidde
Nyland Stichting, Kerkstaat
2
Hoorn
Westfries Museum, Rodesteen
1
Leeuwarden
Fries Museum
Leyden
"De Lakenhal" Municipal
Museum, Oude Singel 22

Het Nederlands Leger-en
Wapenmuseum "Generaal
Hoefer," Pesthuislaan 7,
in der Nähe vom Bahnhof
Middleburg
Museum van het Zeeuwsch
Genootschap der Wetenschappen,
Zeeuws Museum, Wagenaar-
straat 1
Rotterdam
Boymans-van Beuningen Museum, Mathenesserlaan 18-20

Historisch Museum, Korte
Hoogotraat 31
Utrecht
Archiepiscopal Museum
(Archibishop's Museum),
Agnietenstraat 1

Centraal Museum der Gemeente
Utrecht (Central Museum),
1 Agnietenstraat, Postbox
2106

Norway

Bergen
Vestlandske Kunstindustri Museum, Nordahl Brunsgate 9
Oslo
Norsk Folkemuseum, Bygdøy,

Poland
Kraków
Muzeum Historyczne Miasta
Krakówa (Historisches Museum der Stadt Kraków)

Muzeum Ksiazat Czartoryskich

w Krakówie

Muzeum Narodowe w
Krakówie, Nationalmuseum,
ul. Manifestu Lipcowego 12
Łódź.
Muzeum Archeologiczne i
Etnograficzne, Plac Wolnosci
13-14
Warsaw
Muzeum Norodowe w
Warszawie

Portugal
Lisbon
Museu Nacional de Arte
Antiga (National Museum of
Ancient Art)

Soviet Union
Leningrad
The Hermitage
Moscow
Armoury Museum, Kremlin

Staatliches Kreml-Museum,
Rüstkammer des Moskauer
Kreml

Spain
Barcelona
Colleccion Rocamora

Municipal Museum of
Decorative Arts

Museo Textil
Burgos
Real Monasterio de las
Hueglas, (The Monastery
of the Hueglas)
Córdoba
Museo Municipal Taurino
y de Artes Típicas (Museum
of Bull Fighters)
Granada
Catedral Museo (Cathedral
Museum)
Madrid
Monasterio de el Escorial
(Monastery of Escorial)

Museo del Palacio (Royal
Palace of Madrid), Palacio de
Oriente

Armería Real (The Royal
Armoury), Plaza de Armas
del Real Palacio

Lázaro Galdiano Museum,
Calle de Serrano, 122

Museo del Ejército, Méndez
Nuñez, 1

Museo del Pueblo Español
(Museum of Spanish Regional
Costumes), Plaza de la
Marina Español, 9

Museo del Traje Español

Museo Taurino (Museum of
Bullfighting), Plaza de Toros
de las Ventas
Sabadell
Museo de la Ciudad de Sabadell
(Museum of the City of
Sabadell), San Antonio, 13
Tarrasa
Museo Municipal Textil Biosca,
San Pablo, 6
Toledo
Hospital de la Santa Cruz
(Hospital of the Holy Cross)

La Catedral Museo (The Cathedral)
Vich
Museo Episcopal de Vich,

Sweden
Fort Kronan
Militarmuseum
Göthenburg
Historiska Museet
Lund
Kulturhistoriska Museet,
Gamlegården och Östarp-
shallen, Östarp
Östersund
Jämtlands Läns Museum,
Museiplan
Stockholm
Hallwylska Museet, Hamnga-
ton 4

Kungl. Armémuseum (The
Royal Army Museum)

Kungl, Husgeradskåmmaren
(The Royal Household Collection), Royal Palace

Kungl. Livrustkammaren (The
Royal Armory)

Nordiska Museet und Skansen,
Djugärden

Riksantikvarieämbetet och
Statens Historiska Museum,
(State Historical Museum),
Storgatan 41
Uppsala
  Cathedral of Uppsala

Switzerland
Bern
  Bernisches Historisches Mu-
  seum, Helvetiaplatz 5
Lucerne
  Historisches Museum
  (Historical Museum), Rathaus
  on the Kornmarkt 3

  Schweiz. Trachtenmuseum,
  Landhouse Utenberg
Olten
  Historisches Museum der
  Stadt Olten, Konradstr. 7

Turkey
Istanbul
  Museum Topkapi-Saray,
  Topkapi Palace

Yugoslavia
Beograd-Kalemegdan
  Vojni Muzej Jna,
Dubrovnik
  Dubrovački Muzej (Dubrovnik
  Museum of History), The
  Rector's Palace

PART II

Institutions

By
Title

Europe

Institutions Arranged by Title

Abbe' de Murbach
  Strasbourg, France

Abbey House Museum
  Leeds, England

Abergavenny and District Museum
  Abergavenny, Wales

Albury Park House
  Guildford, England

Angus Folk Collection
  Glamis, Scotland

Anne of Cleaves House
  Lewes, England

Annex: The Museum Gallery
  Edinburgh, Scotland

Archaeological Institut
  Rhodes, Greece

Archiepiscopal Museum
  Utrecht, The Netherlands

Archives Départementales d'Ille-
et-Vilaine
  Rennes, France

Ard-Mhusaem Na h-Eireann
  Dublin, Ireland

Armagh County Museum
  Armagh, Northern Ireland

Armeria Real
  Madrid, Spain

Armeria Reale
  Turin, Italy

Armouries
  The Tower of London

London, England

Armoury Museum
  Kremlin
  Moscow, Soviet Union

Army School of Physical Training
Museum
  Aldershot, England

Arsenal Museum
  Copenhagen, Denmark

Bankfield Museum and Art Gallery
  Halifax, England

Bayerisches Nationalmuseum
  Munich, Germany

Bernisches Historisches Museum
  Bern, Switzerland

Bethnal Green Museum
  London, England

Bibliothèque Nationale
  Paris, France

Bignor Roman Villa Collection
  Bignor, England

Birmingham City Museum and Art
Gallery
  The Departments of Archaeology,
  Ethnography, and Birmingham
  History
  Birmingham, England

Blair Castle and Atholl Museum
  Blair Atholl, Scotland

Blaize Castle Museum
  Bristol, England

Bomann-Museum Celle

110

Celle, Germany

Border Regiment
The Keep
Carlisle, England

Borough Museum Collections
Abingdon, England

Bowes Museum
Barnard Castle, England

Boymans-van Beuningen Museum
Rotterdam, The Netherlands

Bradford City Art Gallery and
Museums
Bolling Hall Museum
Bradford, England

British Museum
London, England

Bucks County Museum
Aylesbury, England

Burgenländisches Landesmuseum
Eisenstadt, Austria

Canongate Tolbooth Museum
Edinburgh, Scotland

Ca'Rezzonico
Venice, Italy

Castle Museum
York, England

Castle Museum
Pontefract, England

Catedral Museo
Granada, Spain

Catedral Museo
Toledo, Spain

Cathedral
Saint-Bertrand-de-Comminges,
France

Cathedral Museum
Mainz, Germany

Cathedral of Saint-Stephen
Sens, France

Cathedral of Uppsala
Uppsala, Sweden

Centraal Museum der Gemeente
Utrecht
Utrecht, The Netherlands

Central Museum and Art Gallery
Northampton, England

Central North Brabant Museum
's-Hertogenbosch, The Netherlands

Chapelle Royale de Sainte-Anne
Apt, France

Chelmsford and Essex Museum
Chelmsford, England

Cheltenham Art Gallery and
Museum
Cheltenham, England

Christchurch Mansion
Ipswich, England

City Museum
Wakefield, England

City of Glasgow Corporation Art
Gallery and Museum
Glasgow, Scotland

Collection of J. Telfer Dunbar
Edinburgh, Scotland

Collección Rocamora
Barcelona, Spain

County Museum
Carmarthen, Wales

Curtis Museum
Alton, England

"De Lakenhal" Municipal Museum
Leyden, The Netherlands

Deal Museum

Deal, England

Dickens House
London, England

Die Kostümausstellung im K.K.
Österreichischen Museum
Vienna, Austria

Dom-und Diözesanmuseum
Vienna, Austria

Dorset Military Museum
Dorchester, England

Dubrovački Muzej
Dubrovnik, Yugoslavia

Elizabethan House
Totnes, England

Eridge Castle Costume Museum
Guildford, England

Erstes Österreichisches Heimatmuseum für den Bohmerwald
Vienna, Austria

Ethnographisches Museum
Sofia, Bulgaria

Farleigh Castle Museum
Farleigh-Hugerford, England

Fries Museum
Leeuwarden, The Netherlands

Gainsborough Old Hall
Gainsborough, England

Galleria dell'Umbria
Perugia, Italy

Gallery of English Costume
Manchester, England

Gawthorpe Hall
Burnley, England

Geistliche und Weltliche Schatzkammer
Vienna, Austria

Gemeentemuseum de Hidde Nyland
Stichting
Hindeloopen, The Netherlands

Genealogical Office
Dublin, Ireland

Gorey Castle Museum
Jersey, England

Graflich Erbach-Erbach und Wartenberg-Rothifche Rentkammer
Erbach/Odenwald, Germany

Groninger Museum voor Stad en
Lande
Groningen, The Netherlands

Guildhall Museum
London, England

Guille Alles Museum
Guernsey, England

Hallwylska Museet
Stockholm, Sweden

Harris Museum and Art Gallery
Preston, England

Hatfield House
Hatfield, England

Heeresgeschichtliches Museum
Vienna, Austria

Heimatmuseum
Stendal, Germany

Heimatmuseum
Vienna, Austria

Heimatmuseum Egg
Vorarlberg, Austria

Hereford City Museum and Art
Gallery
Hereford, England

Herefordshire Light Infantry Regimental Museum
Hereford, England

Hermitage
Leningrad, Soviet Union

Hessiches Landesmuseum
Kassel, Germany

Het Nederlands Leger-en Wapenmuseum "Generaal Hoefer"
Leyden, The Netherlands

Highland Folk Museum
Kingussie, Scotland

Historisch Museum
Rotterdam, The Netherlands

Historisches Museum
Dresden, Germany

Historisches Museum
Lucerne, Switzerland

Historisches Museum
Speyer, Germany

Historisches Museum der Stadt
Olten
Olten, Switzerland

Historisches Museum der Stadt
Wien
Vienna, Austria

Historisches Museum und
Munzkabinett
Frankfurt-am-Main, Germany

Historiska Museet
Göthenburg, Sweden

Hospital de la Santa Cruz
Toledo, Spain

Hôtel-Dieu Museum
Beaune, France

Hove Museum of Art
Hove, England

Huntley House Museum
Edinburgh, Scotland

Hüttenberger Heimatmuseum
Leihgestern, Germany

Imperial War Museum
London, England

Ipswich Museum
Ipswich, England

Jämtlands Läns Museum
Östersund, Sweden

Kaiser-Friedrich-Museum
Berlin, Germany

Kärntner Landesmuseum
Klagenfurt, Austria

Kings's Own Regimental Museum
Lancaster, England

Kostümforschungs Institut
Munich, Germany

Kostüm-Sammlung der Akademie
der bildenden Künste
Vienna, Austria

Kulturhistoriska Museet
Lund, Sweden

Kungl. Armémuseum
Stockholm, Sweden

Kungl. Husgerådskammaren
Stockholm, Sweden

Kungl. Livrustkammaren
Stockholm, Sweden

Kungstgew.-Museum
Budapest, Hungary

Kunsthistorisches Museum
Vienna, Austria

Laing Art Gallery and Museum
Newcastle-upon-Tyne, England

Landesmuseum
Schleswig, Germany

Lázaro Galdiano Museum
Madrid, Spain

Lichfield Art Gallery and Museum
    Lichfield, England

Lincoln City and County Museum
    Lincoln, England

Londesborough Barracks
    Hull, England

London Irish Rifles Museum
    London, England

London Museum
    London, England

Ludlow Museum
    Ludlow, England

Luton Museum and Art Gallery
    Luton, England

Militarmuseum
    Fort Kronan, Sweden

Monumenti Musei e Gallerie
Pontificie
    Rome, Italy

Monasterio de el Escorial
    Escorial, Spain

Municipal Museum of Decorative
Arts
    Barcelona, Spain

Musée Agathois
    Agde, France

Musée Alsaçien
    Strasbourg, France

Musée Basque
    Bayonne, France

Musée Bigouden
    Point-l'Abbé, France

Musée Bourguignon Perrin de
Puycousin
    Tournus, France

Musée Carnavalet
    Paris, France

Musée Crozatier
    Le Puy-en-Velay, France

Musée Danicourt
    Péronne, France

Musée de Bretagne
    Rennes, France

Musée de Cluny
    Paris, France

Musée de la Maison d'Ozé
    Alençon, France

Musée de la Marine
    Paris, France

Musée de la Préfecture de Police
    Paris, France

Musée de la Princerie
    Verdun, France

Musée de la Vallée Noire
    La Châtre, France

Musée de la Vénerie
    Senlis, France

Musée de l'Armée
    Paris, France

Musée de l'Historie de France
    Paris, France

Musée de l'Homme
    Paris, France

Musée de l'Oeuvre Notre-Dame
    Strasbourg, France

Musée de Préhistoire
    Les Eyzies, France

Musée Départmental Breton
    Quimper, France

Musée des Antiquités Nationales
    Saint-German-en-Laye, France

Musée des Arts Décoratifs
    Paris, France

Musée des Arts Décoratifs et
d'Art Populaire Régional
   Nantes, France

Musée des Arts et Traditions
Populaires
   Paris, France

Musée des Beaux-Arts
   Clermont-Ferrand, France

Musée des Beaux-Arts
   Dijon, France

Musée des Beaux-Arts
   Honfleur, France

Musée des Beaux-Arts
   Le Mans, France

Musée des Beaux-Arts
   Mâcon, France

Musée des Beaux-Arts
   Troyes, France

Musée des Hautes-Alpes
   Gap, France

Musée des Tissus d'Art et du
Costume Ancien
   Tourcoing, France

Musée de Tessé
   Le Mans, France

Musée du Berry
   Bourges, France

Musée du Costume de la ville
de Paris
   Paris, France

Musée du Donjon
   Niort, France

Musée du Louvre
   Paris, France

Musée du Vieux-Montmartre
   Paris, France

Musée du Vieux Reims

Reims, France

Musée du Vin de Champagne
   Épernay, France

Musée Dunois
   Beaugency, France

Musée Fontenille-Mondiére
   Thiers, France

Musée Fragonard
   Grasse, France

Musée Historique
   Clermont-Ferrand, France

Musée Historique
   Mulhouse, France

Musée Historique
   Obernai, France

Musée Historique
   Strasbourg, France

Musée Historique des Tissus
   Lyon, France

Musée Historique Lorrain
   Nancy, France

Musée Industriel et Agricole
   Lille, France

Musée Local de l'Art Provencal
   Château-Gombert, France

Musée Lyonnais des Arts Décoratifs
   Lyon, France

Musée Maraichin
   Croix-de-Vie, France

Musée Masséna
   Nice, France

Musée Militaire
   Fontainebleau, France

Musée Municipal
   Agen, France

Musée Municipal
  Chartres, France

Musée Municipal
  Séte, France

Musée Municipal de l'Évêché
  Limoges, France

Musée Normand d'Ethnographie
et d'Art Populaire du Vieux-
Honfleur
  Honfleur, France

Musée Paul Dupuy
  Toulouse, France

Musée Perrin de Puycousin
  Dijon, France

Musée Postal Neerlandais
  The Hague, The Netherlands

Musée Préhistorique
  Carnac, France

Musée Pyrénéen
  Lourdes, France

Musée Régional
  Sarrebourg, France

Musée Régional Béarnais
  Pau, France

Musée Royaux d'Armes et
d'Armures
  Brussels, Belgium

Musée Royaux d'Art et d'Histoire
  Brussels, Belgium

Musée Saint-Raymond
  Toulouse, France

Musée Serret et de la Vallée
de Saint-Amarin
  Saint-Amarin, France

Musée Unterlinden
  Colmar, France

Museo Civico

Rieti, Italy

Museo Correr
  Venice, Italy

Museo de la Ciudad de Sabadell
  Sabadell, Spain

Museo del Ejército
  Madrid, Spain

Museo del Pueblo Español
  Madrid, Spain

Museo del Risorgimento
  Milan, Italy

Museo del Risorgimento
  Venice, Italy

Museo del Traje Español
  Madrid, Spain

Museo della Baslica di S.
Ambrogio
  Milan, Italy

Museo Episcopal de Vich
  Vich, Spain

Museo Filangieri
  Naples, Italy

Museo Milano
  Milan, Italy

Museo Municipal Taurino y de
Artes Tipicas
  Córdoba, Spain

Museo Municipal Textil Biosca
  Tarrasa, Spain

Museo Naval
  Milan, Italy

Museo Nazionale
  Florence, Italy

Museo Nazionale di Capodimonte
  Naples, Italy

Museo Palacio Real

Madrid, Spain

Museo Sacro de Biblioteca
Vaticano
Rome, Italy

Museo Simon van Gijn
Dordrecht, The Netherlands

Museo Stibbert
Florence, Italy

Museo Storico Navale
Venice, Italy

Museo Taurino
Madrid, Spain

Museo Textil
Barcelona, Spain

Museu Nacional de Arte Antiga
Lisbon, Portugal

Museum de Waag
Deventer, The Netherlands

Museum der Stadt Lüdenscheid
Lüdenscheid, Germany

Museum für Hamburgische
Geschichte
Hamburg, Germany

Museum für Kunst und Gewerbe
Hamburg, Germany

Museum für Völkerkunde
Berlin, Germany

Museum für Völkerkunde und
Vorgeschichte
Hamburg, Germany

Museum of Childhood
Edinburgh, Scotland

Museum of Childhood and
Costume
Blithfield, England

Museum of Costume
Bath, England

Museum of Precious Stones
Florence, Italy

Museum of Welsh Antiquities
Bangor, Wales

Museum Topkapi-Saray
Istanbul, Turkey

Muzeum Archeologiczne i
Ethnograficzne
Lodź, Poland

Muzeum Historyczne Miasta
Krakówa
Kraków, Poland

Muzeum Ksiazat Czartoryskich w
Krakówie
Kraków, Poland

Muzeum Narodowe w Krakówie
Kraków, Poland

Muzeum Narodowe w Krakówie
Warsaw, Poland

National Army Museum
Camberley, England

National Maritime Museum
London, England

Nationalmuseum
Budapest, Hungary

National Museum
Copenhagen, Denmark

National Museum
Nürnberg, Germany

National Museum of Antiquities of
Scotland
Edinburgh, Scotland

Nederlands Kostuummuseum
The Hague, The Netherlands

Nederlandsch Historisch Scheepvaart Museum
Amsterdam, The Netherlands

117

Newarke House
  Leicester, England

Niedersächsische Landesgalerie
  Hannover, Germany

Niederösterreichisches Landesmuseum
  Vienna, Austria

Nordiska Museet und Skansen
  Stockholm, Sweden

Norsk Folkemuseum
  Oslo, Norway

Nottingham City Museum and
Art Gallery
  Nottingham, England

Öberosterreichisches Landesmuseum
  Linz, Austria

Österreichisches Museum für
angewandte Kunst
  Vienna, Austria

Österreichisches Museum für
Völkskunde
  Vienna, Austria

Paisley Museum and Art Gallery
  Paisley, Scotland

Penhurst Place
  Tonbridge, England

Permanent Exhibition of
Corsican Costumes
  Corsica, France

Pittencrieff House Museum
  Dunfermline, Scotland

Preston Hall Museum and Art
Gallery
  Stockton-on-Tees, England

Quic-en-Groigne Gallery
  Saint Malo, France

Railway Museum

York, England

Rapallo House Museum and Art
Gallery
  Llandudno, Wales

Real Monasterio de las Hueglas
  Burgos, Spain

Red House Museum and Art
Gallery
  Christchurch, England

Regimental Museum
  Newcastle-upon-Tyne, England

Rijksmuseum
  Amsterdam, The Netherlands

Rijksmuseum voor Völkskunde
  Arnhem, The Netherlands

Rijksmuseum Zuiderzeemuseum
  Enkhuizen, The Netherlands

Riksantikvarieämbetet och
  Stockholm, Sweden

Rosenborg Castle
  Copenhagen, Denmark

Rotherham Museum and Art
Gallery
  Rotherham, England

Royal Fusiliers
  London, England

Royal Welch Fusiliers
  Caernarvon, Wales

St. Edward's Hall Museum
  Stow-on-the-Wold, England

St. John's House
  Warwick, England

Salisbury, South Wilts, and
Blackmore Museum
  Salisbury, England

Schlesisches Heimatmuseum und
viele weitere Heimatmuseen

Vienna, Austria

Schweiz. Trachtenmuseum
Lucerne, Switzerland

Scott Polar Research Institute
Cambridge, England

Scottish United Services Museum
Edinburgh, Scotland

Skive Museum
Copenhagen, Denmark

Staatliches Kreml-Museum
Moscow, Soviet Union

Steirisches Völkskundemuseum
Graz, Austria

Sudley Art Gallery and Museum
Liverpool, England

Temple Newsam House
Leeds, England

Tiroler Völkskunstmuseum
Innsbrück, Austria

Tower of London
London, England

Ulster Museum
Belfast, Northern Ireland

Vestlandske Kuntsindustri
Museum
Bergen, Norway

Victoria and Albert Museum
London, England

Vojni Muzej Jna
Beograd-Kalemegdan,
Yugoslavia

Völkskundliche Sammlung des
Salzburger Museums
Salsburg, Austria

Vorarlberger Landesmuseum
Bregenz, Austria

Wallace Collection
London, England

Warwick Castle Museum
Warwick, England

Wellington Museum
London, England

Welsh Folk Museum
Cardiff, Wales

Westfield Museum
Kettering, England

Westfries Museum
Hoorn, The Netherlands

Westgate Museum
Canterbury, England

Westminster Abbey
London, England

Willis Museum
Basingstoke, England

Woburn Abbey
Bletchley, England

Women's Royal Army Corps
Regimental Museum
Lingfield, England

Worthing Museum and Art Gallery
Worthing, England

Zeeuws Museum
Middleburg, The Netherlands

PART II

Institutions

By

Clothing and Clothing Accessory

Europe

Master Code

c	-	Century A.D.
B.C.	-	Century B.C.
A	-	Casual clothing
B	-	Formal clothing
C	-	Children's clothing
E	-	Ecclesiastical vestments
F	-	Female clothing
H	-	Headdress
J	-	Jewelry
M	-	Male clothing
N	-	National clothing
P	-	Professional clothing
R	-	Regional clothing
S	-	Accessories
T	-	Civil clothing
U	-	Unclassified clothing as to century
X	-	Military uniforms
Y	-	Armor
Z	-	Ceremonial clothing

ACCESSORIES

Accessory Code

c	-	Century
C	-	Children
F	-	Female
M	-	Male
U	-	Unclassified as to century

122

Accessories - Armor
British Isles, United
Kingdom
Guildhall Museum, London,
England cf. p.99 1c; M,
2c; M
Wallace Collection, London,
England cf. p.99 14c; M,
15c; M, 16c; M, 17c; M,
18c; M, 19c; M

Accessories - Ceremonial
British Isles, United
Kingdom
Hatfield House, Hatfield,
England cf. p.99 16c; F
Wallace Collection, London,
England cf. p.99 19c; M,
20c; M

Accessories - Ceremonial
Continental Europe
Musée Fontenille-Mondiére,
Thiers, France cf. p.103
19c; F
Rosenborg Castle, Copenhagen,
Denmark cf. p.101 17c;
F-M, 19c; F-M

Accessories - Civil
Continental Europe
Musée Fontenille-Mondiére,
Thiers, France cf. p.103
19c; M
Museo Civico, Rieti, Italy
cf. p.104 18c; M, 19c; M

Accessories - Ecclesiastical
British Isles, United
Kingdom
City of Glasgow Corporation Art
Gallery and Museum, Glas-
gow, Scotland cf. p.101
U; M
Guildhall Museum, London,

England cf. p.99 15c; M,
16c; M

Accessories - Ecclesiastical
Continental Europe
Centraal Museum, Utrecht, The
Netherlands cf. p.105 14c; M
Musée Historique des Tissus, Lyon,
France cf. p.102 13c; M, 14c;
M, 15c; M, 16c; M, 17c; M,
18c; M, 19c; M
Musée Lyonnais des Arts Décor-
atifs, Lyon, France cf. p.102
16c; M
Musée Paul Dupuy, Toulouse,
France cf. p.103 18c; M, 19c;
M

Accessories - Formal and Casual
British Isles, Ireland
Ard-Mhúsaem Na h-Éireann, Dublin,
Ireland cf. p.98 18c; F, 19c;
F

Accessories - Formal and Casual
British Isles, United Kingdom
British Museum, London, England
cf. p.99 13c; F-M
Central Museum and Art Gallery,
Northampton, England cf. p.100
U; F-M
Castle Museum, York, England
cf. p.100 18c; F, 19c; F-M,
20c; F-M
Gallery of English Costume, Manchester, England cf. p.100
16c; F-M, 17c; F-M, 18c; F-M,
19c; F-M, 20c; F-M
Gawthorpe Hall, Burnley, England
cf. p.98 U; F-M
Guildhall Museum, London, England
cf. p.99 1c; F-M, 2c; F-M,
3c; F-M, 4c; F-M, 5c; F-M,
6c; F-M, 7c; F-M, 8c; F-M,
9c; F-M, 10c; F-M, 11c; F-M,

12c; F-M, 13c; F-M, 14c;
F-M, 15c; F-M, 16c; F-M,
17c; F-M, 18c; F-M, 19c;
F-M

Laing Art Gallery and Museum,
Newcastle-upon-Tyne, England cf. p.100 18c; F, 19c;
F

London Museum, London, England cf. p.99 15c; F-M,
16c; M, 17c; F-M, 18c; F-
M, 19c; F-M, 20c; F-M

Luton Museum and Art Gallery,
Luton, England cf. p.100
19c; F, 20c; F

Museum of Childhood and Costume, Blithfield, England
cf. p.98 18c; F-M, 19c;
F-M, U; C-F-M

Museum of Costume, Bath,
England cf. p.98 U; F-M

National Museum of Antiquities
of Scotland, Edinburgh, Scotland cf. p.100 18c; F-M,
19c; F, U; F-M

Red House Museum and Art
Gallery, Christchurch, England cf. p.98 19c; F

Royal Welch Fusiliers, Caernarvon, Wales cf. p.101 17c;
M

Victoria and Albert Museum,
London, England cf. p.99
16c; F-M, 17c; F-M, 18c;
F, 19c; F

Welsh Folk Museum, Cardiff,
Wales cf. p.101 18c; F-M,
19c; F-M

Westfield Museum, Kettering,
England cf. p.99 U; F-M

Accessories - Formal and
Casual
Continental Europe
Armoury Museum, Moscow,
Soviet Union cf. p.106 17c;
F, 18c; F, 19c; F

Bernisches Historisches Museum, Bern, Switzerland cf.
p.107 U; F-M

Boymans-van Beuningen, Rotterdam, The Netherlands cf.
p.105 17c; F-M, 20c; C-F

Centraal Museum, Utrecht, The
Netherlands cf. p.105 14c;
F, 17c; F-M, 18c; F-M, 19c;
F-M, 20c; F

Collección Rocamora, Barcelona,
Spain cf. p.106 U; F-M

Dubrovački Muzej, Dubrovnik,
Yugoslavia cf. p.107 18c; F-M

Groningen Museum voor Stad en
Lande, Groningen, The Netherlands cf. p.105 15c; F-M,
18c; F, 19c; F

Hermitage, Leningrad, Soviet
Union cf. p.106 7 B.C.;
F-M, 6 B.C.; F-M, 5 B.C.;
F-M, 4 B.C.; F-M, 3 B.C.;
F-M, 2 B.C.; F-M

Musée Alsaçien, Strasbourg,
France cf. p.103 19c; F-M

Musée de l'Histoire de France,
Paris, France cf. p.103 18c;
F-M, 19c; F-M

Musée Départmental Breton, Quimper, France cf. p.103 19c;
F-M, 20c; F-M

Musée du Costume de la ville de
Paris, Paris, France cf. p.
102 16c; F-M, 17c; F-M, 18c;
F-M, 19c; F-M, 20c; F-M

Musée du Donjon, Niort, France
cf. p.102 19c; F-M, 20c; F-M

Musée Fontenille-Mondiére, Thiers,
France cf. p.103 19c; F-M

Musée Local de l'Art Provencal,
Château-Gombert, France cf.
p.101 17c; M, 18c; C-F-M,
19c; C-F-M, 20c; C-F-M

Musée Royaux d'Art et d'Histoire,
Brussels, Belgium cf. p.97
18c; M, 19c; M

Musées de Clermont-Ferrand:
Musée des Beaux-Arts and Musée
Historique, Clermont-Ferrand,
France cf. p.101 1c; F, 17c;
F-M, 19c; F-M, 20c; F-M

Museo Municipal Textil Biosca,
Tarrasa, Spain cf. p.106 16c;
F, 17c; F, 18c; F-M

Museum de Waag, Deventer, The
Netherlands cf. p.105 18c; F,
19c; F

Nederlandsch Historisch Scheepvaart Museum, Amsterdam, The

Netherlands cf. p. 105 U; F
Rijksmuseum, Amsterdam, The
Netherlands cf. p. 105 16c;
F, 17c; F, 18c; F, 19c; F-M
Rosenborg Castle, Copenhagen,
Denmark cf. p. 101 17c;
F-M, 19c; F
Zeeuws Museum, Middleburg,
The Netherlands cf. p. 105
19c; C-F-M, 20c; C-F-M

Accessories - Military
British Isles, United Kingdom
Armagh County Museum, Armagh,
Northern Ireland cf. p. 100
U; M
Borough Museum Collections,
Abingdon, England cf. p. 98
U; M
Castle Museum, York, England
cf. p. 100 17c; M, 18c; M,
19c; M, 20c; M, U; M
Castle, The, Carlisle, England
cf. p. 98 19c; M, 20c; M
Gorey Castle Museum, Jersey,
England cf. p. 99 U; M
Herefordshire Light Infantry
Regimental Museum, Here-
ford, England cf. p. 99 U;
M
King's Own Regimental Museum,
Lancaster, England cf. p.
99 U; M
Londesborough Barracks, Hull,
England cf. p. 99 U; M
London Irish Rifles Museum,
London, England cf. p. 99
U; M
Museum of Childhood and Cos-
tume, Blithfield, England
cf. p. 98 18c; M, 19c; M

Accessories - Military
Continental Europe
Heeresgeschichtliches Museum,
Vienna, Austria cf. p. 97
16c; M, 17c; M, 18c; M,
19c; M, 20c; M
Musée Militaire, Fontainebleau,
France cf. p. 102 18c; M,
19c; M
Musée Normand d'Ethnographie

et d'Art Populaire du Vieux-
Honfleur, Honfleur, France
cf. p. 102 18c; M
Museo Naval, Milan, Italy cf. p.
p. 104 U; M
Vojni Muzej Jna, Beograd-Kalemeg-
dan, Yugoslavia cf. p. 107 18c;
M, 19c; M, 20c; M

ARMOR

Armor Code

c - Century
M - Male
U - Unclassified as to century

Armor
British Isles, United Kingdom
Armouries, London, England cf.
p. 99 19c; M, 20c; M
Blair Castle and Atholl Museum,
Blair Atholl, Scotland cf. p. 100
U; M
Canongate Tolbooth Museum, Edin-
burgh, Scotland cf. p. 100 20c;
M
Castle Museum, Pontefract, Eng-
land cf. p. 100 U; M
Castle Museum, York, England
cf. p. 100 16c; M, 17c; M, 18c;
M
City of Glasgow Corporation Art
Gallery and Museum, Glasgow,
Scotland cf. p. 101 15c; M,
16c; M
Farleigh Castle Museum, Farleigh-
Hungerford, England cf. p. 98
U; M
Guildhall Museum, London, England
cf. p. 99 1c; M, 2c; M
Hatfield House, Hatfield, England
cf. p. 99 16c; M, 17c; M
Huntley House Museum, Edinburgh,
Scotland cf. p. 100 17c; M
Laing Art Gallery and Museum,
Newcastle-upon-Tyne, England
cf. p. 100 U; M
Lichfield Art Gallery and Museum,
Lichfield, England cf. p. 99 U;
M
Lincoln City and County Museum,
Lincoln, England cf. p. 99 U;

M

London Museum, London, England cf. p. 99 16c; M, 17c; M

Ludlow Museum, Ludlow, England cf. p. 99 U; M

Penhurst Place, Tonbridge, England cf. p. 100 16c; M, 17c; M

Preston Hall Museum and Art Gallery, Stockton-on-Tees, England cf. p. 100 U; M

Rapallo House Museum and Art Gallery, Llandudno, Wales cf. p. 101 U; M

St. Edward's Hall Museum, Stow-on-the-Wold, England cf. p. 100 U; M

Wallace Collection, London, England cf. p. 99 9c; M, 10c; M, 11c; M, 12c; M, 13c; M, 14c; M, 15c; M, 16c; M, 17c; M, 18c; M, 19c; M, 20c; M, U; M

Warwick Castle Museum, Warwick, England cf. p. 100 15c; M

Westgate Museum, Canterbury, England cf. p. 98 U; M

Armor
Continental Europe
Armeria Real, Madrid, Spain cf. p. 106 U; M

Armeria Reale, Turin, Italy cf. p. 105 U; M

Armoury Museum, Moscow, Soviet Union cf. p. 106 13c; M, 14c; M, 15c; M, 16c; M

Arsenal Museum, Copenhagen, Denmark cf. p. 101 U; M

Graflich Erbach-Erbach und Wartenberg-Rothifche Rentkammer, Erbach/Odenwald, Germany cf. p. 104 U; M

Hermitage, Leningrad, Soviet Union cf. p. 106 15c; M, 16c; M, 17c; M, 18c; M

Musée de l'Armée, Paris, France cf. p. 102 14c; M, 15c; M, 16c; M, 17c; M

Musée des Beaux-Arts, Dijon,

France cf. p. 102 U; M

Musée Historique, Clermont-Ferrand, France cf. p. 101 17c; M, 18c; M, 19c; M, 20c; M

Musée Municipal, Agen, France cf. p. 101 U; M

Musée Municipal, Chartres, France cf. p. 101 U; M

Musée Royaux d'Armes et d'Armures, Brussels, Belgium cf. p. 97 U; M

Musée Royaux d'Art et d'Histoire, Brussels, Belgium cf. p. 98 18c; M, 19c; M

Museo del Ejército, Madrid, Spain cf. p. 106 U; M

Museo del Pueblo Español, Madrid, Spain cf. p. 106 16c; M

Museo Filangieri, Naples, Italy cf. p. 104 U; M

Museo Nazionale, Florence, Italy cf. p. 104 16c; M, 17c; M, 18c; M, 19c; M

Museo Nazionale di Capodimonte, Naples, Italy cf. p. 104 U; M

Museo del Palacio Real, Madrid, Spain cf. p. 106 U; M

Museo Stibbert, Florence, Italy cf. p. 104 15c; M, 16c; M

CEREMONIAL CLOTHING

Ceremonial Clothing Code

c - Century
C - Children
F - Female
M - Male
U - Unclassified as to century

Ceremonial Clothing
British Isles, Ireland
Genealogical Office, Dublin, Ireland cf. p. 98 18c; M, 19c; M, U; M

Ceremonial Clothing
British Isles, United Kingdom
Albury Park House, Guildford, England cf. p. 98 U; F

Guildhall Museum, London, England cf. p. 99 19c; M

Hatfield House, Hatfield, England cf. p. 99 16c; F

126

Huntley House Museum, Edinburgh, Scotland cf. p.100 18c; M, 19c; F-M

London Museum, London, England cf. p.99 19c; F-M, 20c; F-M

Red House Museum and Art Gallery, Christchurch, England cf. p.98 19c; F, 20c; F

Wallace Collection, London, England cf. p.99 19c; M, 20c; M

Welsh Folk Museum, Cardiff, Wales cf. p.101 19c; M, 20c; M

Woburn Abbey, Bletchley, England cf. p.98 U; M

Ceremonial Clothing
  Continental Europe

Armoury Museum, Moscow, Soviet Union cf. p.106 14c; F-M

Bomann-Museum Celle, Celle, Germany cf. p.104 19c; M

Boymans-van Beuningen Museum, Rotterdam, The Netherlands cf. p.105 20c; C-F

Cathedral of Saint-Stephen, Sens, France cf. p.103 5c; F-M, 6c; F-M, 7c; F-M

Centraal Museum, Utrecht, The Netherlands cf. p.105 18c; C, 19c; C, 20c; C-M

Dubrovački Muzej, Dubrovnik, Yugoslavia cf. p.107 17c; M, 18c; M

Historisches Museum der Stadt Olten, Olten, Switzerland cf. p.107 18c; M

Jämtlands Läns Museum, Östersund, Sweden cf. p.106 19c; F

Kungl. Husgerådskammaren, Stockholm, Sweden cf. p.106 19c; F-M, 20c; F-M

Kungl. Livrustkammaren, Stockholm, Sweden cf. p.107 16c; M, 17c; M, 18c; F-M, 19c; F-M, 20c; F-M

Kunsthistorisches Museum, Vienna, Austria cf. p.97

U; F-M

Musée de l'Oeuvre Notre-Dame, Strasbourg, France cf. p.103 18c; F

Musée Historique, Obernai, France cf. p.102 U; F-M

Musée Local de l'Art Provencal, Château-Gombert, France cf. p.101 U; C-F-M

Musée Régional Béarnais, Pau, France cf. p.103 19c; F-M

Museo Civico, Rieti, Italy cf. p.104 18c; M, 19c; M

Museo del Palacio, Madrid, Spain cf. p.106 12c; M, 18c; M, 19c; F-M

Museo del Risorgimento, Milan, Italy cf. p.104 18c; M, 19c; M, U; M

Museo Stibbert, Florence, Italy cf. p.104 18c; M, 19c; M

Nordiska Museet und Skansen, Stockholm, Sweden cf. p.107 16c; F-M, 17c; F-M, 18c; F-M, 19c; F-M, 20c; F-M

Real Monasterio de las Hueglas, Burgos, Spain cf. p.106 13c; F-M, 14c; F-M, 15c; F-M, 16c; F-M, 17c; F-M, 18c; F-M, 19c; F-M, 20c; F-M

Rijksmuseum, Amsterdam, The Netherlands cf. p.105 17c; M

Rijksmuseum voor Völkskunde, Arnhem, The Netherlands cf. p.105 18c; C-F-M, 19c; C-F-M, 20c; C-F-M

Rosenborg Castle, Copenhagen, Denmark cf. p.101 16c; C-F-M, 17c; C-F-M, 18c; M, 19c; M

CIVIL UNIFORMS

Civil Uniform Code

c - Century
F - Female
M - Male
U - Unclassified as to century

Civil Uniforms
  British Isles, United Kingdom

Deal Museum, Deal, England cf.

127

p. 98 U; M
Huntley House Museum, Edinburgh, Scotland cf. p.100
18c; M, 19c; M
Imperial War Museum, London, England cf. p.99 20c; F-M
National Museum of Antiquities of Scotland, Edinburgh, Scotland cf. p.100 U; M
Railway Museum, York, England cf. p.100 U; M
Welsh Folk Museum, Cardiff, Wales cf. p.101 19c; F-M, 20c; F-M

Civil Uniforms
 Continental Europe
Bomann-Museum Celle, Celle, Germany cf. p.104 19c; M
Centraal Museum, Utrecht, The Netherlands cf. p.105 20c; M
Dubrovački Muzej, Dubrovnik, Yugoslavia cf. p.107 17c; M
Historisches Museum der Stadt Olten, Olten, Switzerland cf. p.107 18c; M
Kulturhistoriska Museet, Lund, Sweden cf. p.106 18c; F-M, 19c; F-M, 20c; F-M
Kunsthistorisches Museum, Vienna, Austria cf. p.97 U; M
Musée Alsaçien, Strasbourg, France cf. p.103 U; F-M
Musée Basque, Bayonne, France cf. p.101 U; M
Musée de la Préfecture de Police, Paris, France cf. p.103 U; M
Musée du Costume de la ville de Paris, Paris, France cf. p.102 16c; M, 17c; M, 18c; M, 19c; M, 20c; M, U; M
Musée du Louvre, Paris, France cf. p.103 12c; M, 13c; M, 14c; M, 15c; M, 16c; M
Musée Local de l'Art Provencal, Château-Gombert, France cf. p.101 19c; M
Musée Normand d'Ethnographie et d'Art Populaire du Vieux-

Honfleur, Honfleur, France cf. p.102 18c; M
Musée Paul Dupuy, Toulouse, France cf. p.103 18c; M, 19c; M
Musée Postal Neerlandais, The Hague, The Netherlands cf. p.105 19c; M, 20c; F-M
Museo Civico, Rieti, Italy cf. p.104 18c; M, 19c; M
Museo Correr, Venice, Italy cf. p.105 18c; M, 19c; M
Museo del Pueblo Español, Madrid, Spain cf. p.106 18c; M
Museo Municipal Textil Biosca, Tarrasa, Spain cf. p.106 U; F-M
Museo Textil, Barcelona, Spain cf. p.106 18c; M, 19c; M
Nordiska Museet und Skansen, Stockholm, Sweden cf. p.107 18c; M, 19c; M, 20c; M
Norsk Folkemuseum, Oslo, Norway cf. p.105 19c; M, 20c; M
Real Monasterio de las Hueglas, Burgos, Spain cf. p.106 13c; M, 14c; M, 15c; M, 16c; M, 17c; M, 18c; M, 19c; M, 20c; M
Rijksmuseum Amsterdam, The Netherlands cf. p.105 19c; M
Riksantikvarieämbetet och, Stockholm, Sweden cf. p.107 18c; F-M, 19c; F-M, 20c; F-M
Vojni Muzej Jna, Beograd-Kalemegdan, Yugoslavia cf. p.107 19c; M, 20c; M
Westfries Museum, Hoorn, The Netherlands cf. p.105 19c; M
Zeeuws Museum, Middleburg, The Netherlands cf. p.105 19c; M

ECCLESIASTICAL VESTMENTS

Ecclesiastical Vestment Code

c - Century
F - Female
M - Male
U - Unclassified as to century

Ecclesiastical Vestments -Clerical
 British Isles, United Kingdom

128

City of Glasgow Corporation Art
Gallery and Museum, Glas-
gow, Scotland cf. p. 101 U;
M
Guildhall Museum, London, Eng-
land cf. p. 99 15c; M, 16c;
M
Laing Art Gallery and Museum,
Newcastle-upon-Tyne, England
cf. p. 100 18c; M
National Museum of Antiquities
of Scotland, Edinburgh, Scot-
land cf. p. 100 U; M
Victoria and Albert Museum,
London, England cf. p. 99
12c; M, 13c; M, 14c; M,
15c; M, 16c; M, 17c; M,
18c; M

Ecclesiastical Vestments-
Clerical
Continental Europe
Abbe' de Murbach, Strasbourg,
France cf. p. 103 18c; M
Archiepiscopal Museum, Ut-
recht, The Netherlands, cf.
p. 105 11c; M, 12c; M, 13c;
M, 14c; M, 15c; M, 16c; M,
17c; M, 18c; M, 19c; M
Armoury Museum, Moscow,
Soviet Union cf. p. 106 16c;
M
Catedral Museo, Toledo, Spain
cf. p. 106 U; M
Catedral Museo, Granada, Spain
cf. p. 106 15c; M
Cathedral, Saint-Bertrand-de-
Comminges, France cf. p. 103
9c; M, 10c; M, 11c; M, 12c;
M, 13c; M, 14c; M, 15c; M
Cathedral Museum, Mainz,
Germany cf. p. 104 U; M
Cathedral of Saint-Stephen, Sens,
France cf. p. 103 13c; M
Cathedral of Uppsala, Uppsala,
Sweden cf. p. 107 12c; M,
13c; M, 14c; M, 15c; M, 16c;
M, 17c; M, 18c; M, 19c; M,
20c; M
Centraal Museum, Utrecht, The
Netherlands cf. p. 105 14c;
M
Dom-und Diözesanmuseum,

Vienna, Austria cf. p. 97 U; M
Geistliche und Weltliche Schatz-
kammer, Vienna, Austria cf.
p. 97 U; M
Groningen Museum voor Stad en
Lande, Groningen, The Nether-
lands cf. p. 105 16c; M
Historisches Museum der Stadt
Olten, Olten, Switzerland cf.
p. 107 17c; M, 18c; M, 19c; M
Hospital de la Santa Cruz, Toledo,
Spain cf. p. 106 16c; M, 17c;
M, 18c; M
Hôtel-Dieu Museum, Beaune,
France cf. p. 101 15c; F,
16c; F, 17c; F, 18c; F, 19c;
F, 20c; F
Jämtlands Läns Museum, Öster-
sund, Sweden cf. p. 106 15c;
M, 16c; M, 17c; M, 18c; M
Kungl. Livrustkammaren, Stock-
holm, Sweden cf. p. 107 16c;
M, 18c; M, U; M
Monasterio de el Escorial, Madrid,
Spain cf. p. 106 18c; M, 19c;
M
Monumenti Musei e Gallerie Ponti-
ficie, Rome, Italy cf. p. 104
U; M, 13c; M
Musée Historique, Strasbourg,
France cf. p. 103 16c; M,
17c; M, 18c; M
Musée Historique des Tissus,
Lyon, France cf. p. 102 13c;
M, 14c; M, 15c; M, 16c; M,
17c; M, 18c; M; F-M, 19c; M
Musée Lyonnais des Arts Décora-
tifs, Lyon, France cf. p. 102
13c; M, 16c; M, 17c; M, 18c;
M
Musée Normand d'Ethnographie et
d'Art Populaire du Vieux-Hon-
fleur, Honfleur, France cf.
p. 102 16c; M
Musée Paul Dupuy, Toulouse,
France cf. p. 103 18c; M,
19c; M
Musée Royaux d'Art et d'Histoire,
Brussels, Belgium cf. p. 98
15c; M
Museo della Baslica di S. Ambro-
gio, Milan, Italy cf. p. 104
U; M

Museo Episcopal de Vich, Vich, Spain cf. p. 106 U; M

Museo Municipal Textil Biosca, Tarrasa, Spain cf. p. 106 15c; M, 16c; M, 17c; M, 18c; M, 19c; M

Museo del Palacio Real, Madrid, Spain cf. p. 106 18c; M, 19c; M

Museo Sacro de Biblioteca Vaticano, Rome, Italy cf. p. 105 13c; M, 17c; M

Museo Textil, Barcelona, Spain cf. p. 106 13c; M, 14c; M, 15c; M, 16c; M, 17c; M, 18c; M, 19c; M, 20c; M

Museum of Precious Stones, Florence, Italy cf. p. 104 14c; M

Museu Nacional de Arte Antiga, Lisbon, Portugal cf. p. 106 14c; M, 15c; M, 16c; M, 17c; M, 18c; M, 19c; M, U; M

Norsk Folkemuseum, Oslo, Norway cf. p. 105 17c; M, 18c; M, 19c; M, 20c; M

Real Monasterio de las Hueglas, Burgos, Spain cf. p. 106 9c; M, 10c; M, 11c; M, 12c; M, 13c; M, 14c; M, 15c; M

Rijksmuseum, Amsterdam, The Netherlands cf. p. 105 18c; M

Riksantikvarieämbetet och, Stockholm, Sweden cf. p. 107 12c; M, 13c; M, 14c; M, 15c; M, 16c; M, 17c; M, 18c; M, 19c; M, 20c; M

Ecclesiastical Clothing - Lay Continental Europe

Musée Municipal de l'Éveché, Limoges, France cf. p. 102 U; M

FORMAL AND CASUAL CLOTHING

Formal and Casual Clothing Code

c - Century
A - Casual clothing
B - Formal clothing
C - Childrens' clothing
F - Female clothing
M - Male clothing
U - Unclassified as to century

Formal and Casual Clothing British Isles, Ireland

Ard-Mhúsaem Na h-Éireann, Dublin, Ireland cf. p. 98 15c; A-B-F-M, 16c; A-B-F-M, 18c; A-B-F-M, 19c; A-B-F-M

Formal and Casual Clothing British Isles, United Kingdom

Abbey House Museum, Leeds, England cf. p. 99 19c; A-B-F-M

Abergavenny and District Museum, Abergavenny, Wales cf. p. 101 U; A-B-F-M

Angus Folk Collection, Glamis, Scotland cf. p. 101 U; A-B-F-M

Anne of Cleaves House, Lewes, England cf. p. 99 U; A-B-F-M

Annex: The Museum Gallery, Edinburgh, Scotland cf. p. 100 18c; A-B-F-M, 19c; A-B-F-M

Armagh County Museum, Armagh, Northern Ireland cf. p. 100 U; A-B-F-M

Army School of Physical Training Museum, Aldershot, England cf. p. 98 19c; A-M, 20c; A-M

Bankfield Museum and Art Gallery, Halifax, England cf. p. 99 U; A-B-F-M

Bethnal Green Museum, London, England cf. p. 99 U; A-B-F-M

Blaize Castle Museum, Bristol, England cf. p. 98 U; A-B-F-M

Bradford City Art Gallery and Museums, Bradford, England cf. p. 98 19c; A-B-F, U; A-B-F-M

British Museum, London, England cf. p. 99 5c; A-F-M, 6c; A-F-M, 8c; A-F-M, 9c; A-F-M, 13c; A-F-M

130

Bucks County Museum, Aylesbury, England cf. p. 98 U; A-B-F-M

Canongate Tolbooth Museum, Edinburgh, Scotland cf. p. 100 U; A-B-F-M

Castle Museum, York, England cf. p. 100 18c; A-B-F-M, 19c; A-B-F-M, 20c; A-B-F-M

Chelmsford and Essex Museum, Chelmsford, England cf. p. 98 U; A-B-F-M

Cheltenham Art Gallery and Museum, Cheltenham, England cf. p. 98 U; A-B-F-M

Christchurch Mansion, Ipswich, England cf. p. 99 U; A-B-F-M

City of Glasgow Corporation Art Gallery and Museum, Glasgow, Scotland cf. p. 101 U; A-B-F-M

City Museum, Wakefield, England cf. p. 100 U; A-B-F-M

Collection of J. Telfer Dunbar, Edinburgh, Scotland cf. p. 100 17c; A-B-F-M, 18c; A-B-F-M

Curtis Museum, Alton, England cf. p. 98 U; A-B-F-M

Deal Museum, Deal, England cf. p. 98 U; A-B-M

Elizabethan House, Totnes, England cf. p. 100 U; A-B-F-M

Eridge Castle, Costume Museum, Guildford, England cf. p. 98 U; A-B-F-M

Gallery of English Costume, Manchester, England cf. p. 100 16c; A-B-F-M, 17c; A-B-F-M, 18c; A-B-F-M, 19c; A-B-F-M, 20c; A-B-F-M

Gawthorpe Hall, Burnley, England cf. p. 98 U; A-B-F-M

Guildhall Museum, London, England cf. p. 99 1c; A-F-M, 2c; A-F-M, 3c; A-F-M, 4c; A-F-M, 5c; A-F-M, 6c; A-F-M, 7c; A-F-M, 8c; A-F-M, 9c; A-F-M, 10c; A-F-M, 11c; A-F-M, 12c; A-F-M, 13c; A-F-M, 14c; A-F-M, 15c; A-B-F-M, 16c; A-B-F-M, 17c; A-B-F-M, 18c; A-B-F-M, 19c; B-F-M

Guille Alles Museum, Guernsey, England cf. p. 98 U; A-B-F-M

Harris Museum and Art Gallery, Preston, England cf. p. 100 19c; A-B-F-M

Hereford City Museum and Art Gallery, Hereford, England cf. p. 99 U; A-B-F-M

Highland Folk Museum, Kingussie, Scotland cf. p. 101 U; A-B-F-M

Hove Museum of Art, Hove, England cf. p. 99 U; A-B-F-M

Huntley House Museum, Edinburgh, Scotland cf. p. 100 18c; B-F, 19c; B-F

Ipswich Museum, Ipswich, England cf. p. 99 U; A-B-F-M

Laing Art Gallery and Museum, Newcastle-upon-Tyne, England cf. p. 100 18c; A-F-M, 19c; A-F-M, 20c; A-F

London Museum, London, England cf. p. 99 16c; A-B-F-M, 17c; A-B-F-M, 18c; A-B-F-M, 19c; A-B-F-M, 20c; A-B-F-M

Luton Museum and Art Gallery, Luton, England cf. p. 100 19c; A-F-M, 20c; A-F-M

Museum of Childhood, Edinburgh, Scotland cf. p. 100 18c; A-B-C, 19c; A-B-C

Museum of Childhood and Costume, Blithfield, England cf. p. 98 18c; A-B-F-M, 19c; A-B-F-M, U; A-B-C-F-M

Museum of Costume, Bath, England cf. p. 98 U; A-B-F-M

Museum of Welsh Antiquities, Bangor, Wales cf. p. 101 U; A-B-F-M

National Maritime Museum, London, England cf. p. 99 19c; A-B-M

National Museum of Antiquities of Scotland, Edinburgh, Scotland cf. p. 100 17c; A-B-F-M, 18c; A-B-F-M, 19c; A-B-F-M, U; A-B-F-M

Newarke House, Leicester, England cf. p. 99 U; A-B-F-M

Nottingham City Museum and
Art Gallery, Nottingham,
England cf. p.100 U; A-B-
F-M

Paisley Museum and Art Gallery, Paisley, Scotland cf.
p.101 19c; A-B-F

Pittencrieff House Museum,
Dunfermline, Scotland cf.
p.100 19c; A-B-F-M

Red House Museum and Art
Gallery, Christchurch, Eng-
land cf. p.98 18c; A-B-F-
M, 19c; A-B-F-M, 20c; A-
B-F

St. John's House, Warwick,
England cf. p.100 U; A-
B-F-M

Salisbury, South Wilts and
Blackmore Museum, Salis-
bury, England cf. p.100
U; A-B-F-M

Scott Polar Research Institute,
Cambridge, England cf. p.
98 U; A-B-F-M

Sudley Art Gallery and Museum,
Liverpool, England cf. p.
99 U; A-B-F-M

Temple Newsam House, Leeds,
England cf. p.99 18c; A-B-
F-M, 19c; A-B-F-M

Ulster Museum, Belfast, Northern Ireland cf. p.100 19c;
A-B-F-M

Victoria and Albert Museum,
London, England cf. p.99
16c; A-B-F-M, 17c; A-B-F-
M, 18c; A-B-F-M, 19c; A-
B-F-M, 20c; A-B-F

Wallace Collection, London,
England cf. p.99 17c; A-M

Warwick Castle Museum, Warwick, England cf. p.100 U;
A-B-F-M

Welsh Folk Museum, Cardiff,
Wales cf. p.101 18c; A-C-
F-M, 19c; A-B-C-F-M, 20c;
B-M

Willis Museum, Basingstoke,
England cf. p.98 U; A-B-
F-M

Worthing Museum and Art Gallery, Worthing, England cf.

p.100 U; A-B-F-M

Formal and Casual Clothing
Continental Europe

Archaeological Institut, Rhodes,
Greece cf. p.104 U; A-B-F-M

Archives Départementales d'Ille-
et-Vilaine, Rennes, France
cf. p.103 U; A-B-F-M

Armoury Museum, Moscow,
Soviet Union cf. p.106 14c;
A-B-F-M, 16c; A-B-F-M, 17c;
A-B-F-M, 18c; A-B-F-M, 19c;
A-B-F-M

Bayerisches Nationalmuseum,
Munich, Germany cf. p.104
16c; A-B-F-M, 17c; A-B-F-M,
18c; A-B-F-M, 19c; A-B-F-M,
U; A-B-F-M

Bernisches Historisches Museum,
Bern, Switzerland cf. p.107
15c; A-B-F-M, 16c; A-B-F-M,
19c; A-B-F-M, U; A-B-F-M

Bomann-Museum Celle, Celle,
Germany cf. p.104 18c; A-B-
F-M, 19c; A-B-F-M

Boymans-van Beuningen Museum,
Rotterdam, The Netherlands
cf. p.105 20c; A-B-C-F

Burgenländisches Landesmuseum,
Eisenstadt, Austria cf. p.97
U; A-B-F-M

Ca'Rezzonico, Venice, Italy cf.
p.105 17c; A-B-C-F-M

Centraal Museum, Utrecht, The
Netherlands cf. p.105 14c;
A-F, 17c; A-C-M, 18c; A-B-C-
F-M, 19c; A-B-C-F-M, 20c;
A-B-C-F

Central North Brabant Museum,
's-Hertogenbosch, The Netherlands cf. p.105 16c; A-F,
17c; A-B-F-M, 18c; A-B-F-M,
U; A-F

Collección Rocamora, Barcelona,
Spain cf. p.106 A-B-F-M

"De Lakenhal" Municipal Museum,
Leyden, The Netherlands, cf.
p.105 18c; A-B-F-M, 19c; A-
B-F-M

Die Kostümausstellung im K. K.
Österreichischen Museum,
Vienna, Austria cf. p.97 16c;

132

A-B-F-M, 17c; A-B-F-M, 19c; A-B-F-M, U; A-B-F-M
Dubrovački Muzej, Dubrovnik, Yugoslavia cf. p.107 17c; A-B-F-M, 18c; A-B-F-M
Erstes Österreichisches Heimatmuseum für den Böhmerwald, Vienna, Austria cf. p.97 U; A-B-F-M
Ethnographisches Museum, Sofia, Bulgaria cf. p.101 U; A-B-F-M
Fries Museum, Leeuwarden, The Netherlands cf. p.105 U; A-B-C-F-M
Galleria dell'Umbria, Perugia, Italy cf. p.104 U; A-B-F-M
Gemeentemuseum de Hidde Nyland Stichting, Hindeloopen, The Netherlands cf. p.105 U; A-B-F-M
Groningen Museum voor Stad en Lande, Groningen, The Netherlands cf. p.105 18c; A-F-M, 19c; A-F
Hallwylska Museet, Stockholm, Sweden cf. p.106 U; A-B-F-M
Hatfield House, Hatfield, England cf. p.99 16c; B-F
Heimatmuseum, Stendal, Germany cf. p.104 15c; A-B-F-M, U; A-B-F-M
Heimatmuseum, Vienna, Austria cf. p.97 U; A-B-F-M
Heimatmuseum Egg, Vorarlberg, Austria cf. p.97 U; A-B-F-M
Hessiches Landesmuseum, Kassel, Germany cf. p.104 U; A-B-F-M, 18c; A-B-F-M, 19c; A-B-F-M
Historisch Museum, Rotterdam, The Netherlands cf. p.105 18c; A-B-F-M, 19c; A-B-F-M
Historisches Museum, Dresden, Germany cf. p.104 16c; A-B-F-M, 17c; A-B-F-M, U; A-B-F-M
Historisches Museum, Lucerne, Switzerland cf. p.107 U; A-B-F-M
Historisches Museum, Speyer,

Germany cf. p.104 18c; A-B-F-M, 19c; A-B-F-M, U; A-B-F-M
Historisches Museum der Stadt Olten, Olten, Switzerland cf. p.107 18c; A-B-C-F, 19c; A-B-C-F
Historisches Museum der Stadt Wien, Modesammlungen, Vienna, Austria cf. p.97 18c; A-F-M, 19c; A-F-M
Historisches Museum and Munzkabinett, Frankfurt am Main, Germany cf. p.104 U; A-B-F-M
Historiska Museet, Gothenburg, Sweden cf. p.106 U; A-B-F-M
Huttenberger Heimatmuseum, Leihgestern, Germany cf. p.104 U; A-B-F-M
Jämtlands Läns Museum, Östersund, Sweden cf. p.106 18c; B-F-M, 19c; A-B-F-M, 20c; B-F-M
Kaiser-Friedrich Museum, Berlin, Germany cf. p.103 4c; A-B-F-M, 5c; A-B-F-M, 6c; A-B-F-M, 7c; A-B-F-M, U; A-B-F-M
Kärtner Landesmuseum, Klagenfurt, Austria cf. p.97 U; A-B-F-M
Kostum-Sammlung der Akademie der bildenden Künste, Vienna, Austria cf. p.97 U; A-B-F-M
Kulturhistoriska Museet, Lund, Sweden cf. p.106 18c; A-B-F-M, 19c; A-B-F-M, 20c; A-B-F-M
Kungl. Livrustkammaren, Stockholm, Sweden cf. p.107 17c; A-B-C-F-M, 18c; A-B-C-F-M, 19c; A-B-C-F-M, 20c; A-B-C-F-M
Kungstgew.-Museum, Budapest, Hungary cf. p.104 17c; A-B-F-M, U; A-B-F-M
Landesmuseum für Vor-und Fruhgeschichte von Schleswig-Holstein, Schleswig, Germany cf. p.104 U; A-B-F-M
Milan Museum, Milan, Italy cf. p.104 U; A-B-F-M
Municipal Museum of Decorative

Arts, Barcelona, Spain cf.
p.106   U; A-B-F-M
Musée Agathois, Agde, France
cf. p.101   U; A-B-F-M
Musée Alsaçien, Strasbourg,
France   cf. p.103   19c; A-
F-M
Musée Basque, Bayonne, France
cf. p.101   19c; A-F-M
Musée Bigouden, Pont-l'Abbé,
France   cf. p.103   19c; A-
B-F-M, 20c; A-B-F-M
Musée Bourguignon Perrin de
Puycousin, Tournus, France
cf. p.103   U; A-B-F-M
Musée Carnavalet, Paris,
France   cf. p.102   U; A-B-
F-M
Musée de Bretagne, Rennes,
France   cf. p.103   U; A-B-
F-M
Musée de Cluny, Paris, France
cf. p.102   9c; A-B-F-M, 10c;
A-B-F-M, 11c; A-B-F, M,
12c; A-B-F-M, 13c; A-B-F-
M, 14c; A-B-F-M, 15c; A-
B-F-M
Musée de la Maison d'Ozé,
Alençon, France   cf. p.101
U; A-B-F-M
Musée de la Vallée Noire, La
Chatre, France   cf. p.102
U; A-B-F-M
Musée de la Vénerie, Senlis,
France   cf. p.103   U; A-F-
M
Musée de l'Histoire de France,
Paris, France   cf. p.103
18c; A-F-M, 19c; A-F-M
Musée de l'Homme, Paris,
France   cf. p.103   16c; A-
B-F-M
Musée de l'Oeuvre Notre-Dame,
Strasbourg, France   cf. p.
103   18c; B-F
Musée Départmental Breton,
Quimper, France   cf. p.103
19c; A-B-F-M, 20c; A-B-
F-M
Musée de Préhistoire, Les
Eyzies, France
cf. p.102   1800 B.C. - 1 A.D.;
A-F-M, 1c; A-B-F-M, 2c; A-

B-F-M, 3c; A-B-F-M, 4c; A-
B-F-M
Musée des Arts Décoratifs, Paris,
France   cf. p.102   18c; A-B-
F-M, 19c; A-B-F-M
Musée des Arts Décoratifs et
d'Art Populaire Régional, Nantes,
France   cf. p.102   U; A-B-F-M
Musée des Beaux-Arts, Honfleur,
France   cf. p.102   19c; A-B-F-M
Musée des Beaux-Arts, Mâcon,
France   cf. p.102   U; A-B-F-M
Musée des Tissus d'Art et du
Costume Ancien, Tourcoing,
France   cf. p.103   U; A-B-F-M
Musée du Berry, Bourges, France
cf. p.101   18c; A-B-F-M, 19c;
A-B-F-M
Musée du Costume de la ville de
Paris, Paris, France   cf. p.
102   16c; A-B-C-F-M, 17c; A-
B-C-F-M, 18c; A-B-C-F-M,
19c; A-B-C-F-M, 20c; A-B-C-
F-M
Musée du Donjon, Niort, France
cf. p.102   19c; A-B-F-M, 20c;
A-B-F-M
Musée Dunois, Beaugency, France
cf. p.101   U; A-B-F-M
Musée du Vieux-Montmartre, Paris,
France   cf. p.103   U; A-B-F-M
Musée du Vin de Champagne,
Épernay, France   cf. p.102
U; A-F-M
Musée Fontenille-Mondiére, Thiers,
France   cf. p.103   18c; A-B-F-
M, 19c; A-B-F-M
Musée Fragonard, Grasse, France
cf. p.102   U; A-B-F-M
Musée Historique, Mulhouse, France
cf. p.102   18c; A-B-F-M, 19c;
A-B-F-M
Musée Historique, Obernai, France
cf. p.102   U; A-B-F-M
Musée Historique, Strasbourg,
France   cf. p.103   19c; A-B-F-
M
Musée Historique des Tissus,
Lyon, France   cf. p.102   18c;
A-B-F-M
Musée Historique Lorrain, Nancy,
France   cf. p.102   U; A-B-F-M
Musée Industriel et Agricole,

Lille, France cf. p. 102 U; A-B-F-M

Musée Local de l'Art Provencal, Château-Gombert, France cf. p. 101 17c; A-B-M, 18c; A-B-C-F-M, 19c; A-B-C-F-M, 20c; A-B-C-F-M, U; A-B-C-F-M

Musée Lyonnais des Arts Décoratifs, Lyon, France cf. p. 102 18c; A-F-M

Musée Maraichin, Croix-de-Vie, France cf. p. 102 U; A-B-F-M

Musée Municipal, Séte, France cf. p. 103 U; A-M

Musée Municipal de l'Évêché, Limoges, France cf. p. 102 U; A-M

Musée Normand d'Ethnographie et d'Art Populaire du Vieux-Honfleur, Honfleur, France cf. p. 102 18c; A-B-F-M

Musée Perrin de Puycousin, Dijon, France cf. p. 102 19c; A-B-C-F-M

Musée Régional Béarnais, Pau, France cf. p. 103 19c; A-B-F-M

Musée Royaux d'Art et d'Histoire, Brussels, Belgium cf. p. 98 18c; A-F-M, 19c; A-F-M

Musée Unterlinden, Colmar, France cf. p. 101 U; A-B-F-M

Musées de Clermont-Ferrand: Musée des Beaux-Arts and Musée Historique, Clermont-Ferrand, France cf. p. 101 1c; A-F, 17c; A-F-M, 19c; A-F-M, 20c; A-F-M

Museo de la Ciudad de Sabadell, Sabadell, Spain cf. p. 106 U; A-B-F-M

Museo del Palacio, Madrid, Spain cf. p. 106 12c; B-M, 16c; A-B-F-M, 18c; B-M, 19c; B-F

Museo del Pueblo Español, Madrid, Spain cf. p. 106 17c; A-B-F-M, 18c; A-B-F-M, 19c; A-B-F-M, 20c; A-B-F-M

Museo del Traje Español, Madrid, Spain cf. p. 106 U; A-B-F-M

Museo Municipal Taurino y de Artes Típicas, Córdoba, Spain cf. p. 106 19c; A-B-M, 20c; A-B-M

Museo Municipal Textil Biosca, Tarrasa, Spain cf. p. 106 U; A-B-F-M, 17c; A-B-F-M, 18c; A-B-F-M, 19c; A-B-M

Museo Taurino, Madrid, Spain cf. p. 106 U; A-B-M

Museum de Waag, Deventer, The Netherlands cf. p. 105 18c; B-F, 19c; B-F

Museum der Stadt Lüdenscheid, Lüdenscheid, Germany cf. p. 104 U; A-B-F-M

Museum für Hamburgische Geschichte, Hamburg, Germany cf. p. 104 18c; A-B-F-M, 19c; A-B-F-M, 20c; A-B-F-M

Museum für Kunst und Gewerbe, Hamburg, Germany cf. p. 104 18c; A-B-F-M, U; A-B-F-M

Museum für Völkerkunde, Berlin, Germany cf. p. 103 U; A-B-F-M

Museum für Völkerkunde und Vorgeschichte, Hamburg, Germany cf. p. 104 U; A-B-F-M

Museum Topkapi-Saray, Istanbul, Turkey cf. p. 107 15c; A-B-F-M, 16c; A-B-F-M, U; A-B-F-M

Muzeum Archeologiczne i Etnograficzne, Lodź, Poland cf. p. 106 U; A-B-F-M

Muzeum Historyczne Miasta Krakówa, Kraków, Poland cf. p. 105 U; A-B-F-M

Muzeum Ksiazat Czartoryskich w Krakówie, Kraków, Poland cf. p. 105 16c; A-B-F-M, 17c; A-B-F-M, U; A-B-F-M

Muzeum Narodowe w Krakówie, Kraków, Poland cf. p. 106 18c; A-B-F-M, U; A-B-F-M

Muzeum Narodowe w Warszawie, Warsaw, Poland cf. p. 106 18c; A-B-F-M, U; A-B-F-M

Nationalmuseum, Budapest, Hungary cf. p. 104 19c; A-B-F-M,

20c; A-B-F-M, U; A-B-F-M
National Museum, Copenhagen,
Denmark cf. p. 101 U; A-B-F-M
National Museum, Nürnberg, Germany cf. p. 104 16c; A-B-F-M,
17c; A-B-F-M, 18c; A-B-F-M,
U; A-B-F-M
Nederlands Kostuummuseum, The
Hague, The Netherlands cf. p.
105 16c; A-F-M, 17c; A-B-F-
M, 18c; A-B-F-M, 19c; A-B-F-
M, 20c; A-F-M, U; A-B-F-M
Niedersächsische Landesgalerie,
Hannover, Germany cf. p. 104,
16c; A-B-F-M, 17c; A-B-F-M,
U; A-B-F-M
Niederösterreichisches Landesmuseum, Vienna,Austria cf. p.
97 U; A-B-F-M
Nordiska Museet und Skansen,
Stockholm, Sweden cf. p. 107
16c; A-B-C-F-M, 17c; A-B-C-
F-M, 18c; A-B-C-F-M, 19c; A-
B-C-F-M, 20c; A-B-C-F-M
Norsk Folkemuseum, Oslo, Norway cf. p. 105 18c; A-B-F-M,
19c; A-B-F-M, 20c; A-B-F-M
Öberosterreichisches Landesmuseum, Linz, Austria cf.
p. 97 U; A-B-F-M
Österreichisches Museum für
angewandte Kunst, Vienna,
Austria cf. p. 97 16c; A-
B-F-M, 17c; A-B-F-M, 18c;
A-B-F-M, 19c; A-B-F-M,
20c; A-B-F-M
Österreichisches Museum für
Volkskunde, Vienna, Austria
cf. p. 97 U; A-B-F-M
Permanent Exhibition of Corsican Costumes, Corsica,
France cf. p. 101 U; A-B-
F-M
Quic-en-Groigne Gallery, Saint-
Malo, France cf. p. 103 U;
A-B-F-M
Real Monasterio de las Hueglas,
Burgos, Spain cf. p. 106
13c; B-F-M
Rijksmuseum, Amsterdam, The
Netherlands cf. p. 105 16c;
A-F, 17c; A-B-F-M, 18c; B-
F-M, 19c; A-B-F-M

Rijksmuseum voor Völkskunde,
Arnhem, The Netherlands cf.
p. 105 18c; A-B-C-F-M, 19c;
A-B-C-F-M, 20c; A-B-F-M,
U; A-B-F-M
Rijksmuseum Zuiderzeemuseum,
Enkhuizen, The Netherlands
cf. p. 105 U; A-B-F-M
Riksantikvarieambetet och, Stockholm, Sweden cf. p. 107 18c;
A-B-F-M, 19c; A-B-F-M, 20c;
A-B-F-M
Rosenborg Castle, Copenhagen,
Denmark cf. p. 101 16c; A-B-
C-F-M, 17c; A-B-C-F-M, 18c;
B-M, 19c; A-B-M, 20c; A-B-M
Schlesisches Heimatmuseum und
viele weitere Heimatmuseen,
Vienna, Austria cf. p. 97 U;
A-B-F-M
Schweiz. Trachtenmuseum, Lucerne,
Switzerland cf. p. 107 U; A-B-
F-M
Simon van Gijn Museum, Dordrecht,
The Netherlands cf. p. 105 18c;
A-B-C-F-M, 19c; A-B-C-F-M
Skive Museum, Copenhagen, Denmark cf. p. 101 U; A-B-F-M
Staatliches Kreml-Museum, Moscow, Soviet Union cf. p. 106
17c; A-B-F-M, U; A-B-F-M
Steirisches Völkskundemuseum,
Graz, Austria cf. p. 97 U;
A-B-F-M
Tiroler Völkskunstmuseum, Innsbruck, Austria cf. p. 97 18c;
A-B-F-M, 19c; A-B-F-M, U;
A-B-F-M
Vestlandske Kunstindustri Museum,
Bergen, Norway cf. p. 105 U;
A-B-F-M
Vojni Muzej Jna, Beograd-Kalemegdan, Yugoslavia cf. p. 107
19c; A-M
Völkskundliche Sammlung des
Salzburger Museums, Salsburg,
Austria cf. p. 97 U; A-B-F-M
Kostümforschungs Institut, Munich,
Germany cf. p. 104 16c; A-B-
F-M
Vorarlberger Landesmuseum,
Bregenz, Austria cf. p. 97 U;
A-B-F-M

Westfries Museum, Hoorn, The Netherlands cf. p.105 18c; A-B-F-M, 19c; A-B-F-M
Zeeuws Museum, Middleburg, The Netherlands cf. p.105 19c; A-B-C-F-M, 20c; A-B-C-F-M

HEADDRESSES

Headdress Code

c - Century
C - Children
F - Female
M - Male
U - Unclassified as to century

Headdress - Armor
British Isles, United Kingdom
Armouries, London, England cf. p.99 19c; M, 20c; M
Canongate Tolbooth Museum, Edinburgh, Scotland cf. p. 100 20c; M
Castle Museum, York, England cf. p.100 16c; M, 17c; M, 18c; M
Huntley House Museum, Edinburgh, Scotland cf. p.100 18c; M
London Museum, London, England cf. p.99 16c; M, 17c; M
Wallace Collection, London, England cf. p.99 9c; M, 10c; M, 11c; M, 12c; M, 13c; M, 14c; M, 15c; M, 16c; M, 17c; M, 18c; M, 19c; M, 20c; M

Headdress - Armor
Continental Europe
Hermitage, Leningrad, Soviet Union cf. p.106 18c; M
Musées de Clermont-Ferrand: Musée des Beaux-Arts and Musée Historique, Clermont-Ferrand, France cf. p.101 17c; M, 18c; M, 19c; M, 20c; M

Headdress - Ceremonial
British Isles, United Kingdom
Hatfield House, Hatfield, England cf. p.99 16c; F
London Museum, London, England cf. p.99 19c; F
Wallace Collection, London, England cf. p.99 16c; F-M, 19c; M, 20c; M

Headdress - Ceremonial
Continental Europe
Centraal Museum, Utrecht, The Netherlands cf. p.105 20c; M
Musée Alsaçien, Strasbourg, France cf. p.103 19c; F
Rosenborg Castle, Copenhagen, Denmark cf. p.101 16c; M, 17c; M, 18c; F, 19c; M

Headdress - Civilian
Continental Europe
Museo Civico, Rieti, Italy cf. p.104 18c; M, 19c; M

Headdress - Ecclesiastical
Continental Europe
Cathedral, Saint-Bertrand-de-Comminges, France cf. p.103 13c; M
Centraal Museum, Utrecht, The Netherlands cf. p.105 14c; M
Museo Sacro de Biblioteca Vaticano, Rome, Italy cf. p.105 17c; M
Museu Nacional de Arte Antiga, Lisbon, Portugal cf. p.106 14c; M

Headdress - Formal and Casual
British Isles, United Kingdom
Bradford City Art Gallery and Museum, Bradford, England cf. p.98 19c; F
British Museum, London, England cf. p.99 13c; F
Castle Museum, York, England cf. p.100 18c; F-M, 19c; F-M, 20c; F-M
Guildhall Museum, London, England cf. p.99 16c; M
Hatfield House, Hatfield, England

cf. p. 99 16c; F

Laing Art Gallery and Museum, Newcastle-upon-Tyne, England cf. p. 100 19c; F

London Museum, London, England cf. p. 99 16c; F-M, 17c; F-M, 18c; F-M, 19c; F-M, 20c; F-M

Luton Museum and Art Gallery, Luton, England cf. p. 100 19c; F, 20c; F

Red House Museum and Art Gallery, Christchurch, England cf. p. 98 19c; F

Temple Newsam House, Leeds, England cf. p. 99 19c; F

Victoria and Albert Museum, London, England cf. p. 99 16c; F-M, 18c; F, 19c; F, 20c; F

Welsh Folk Museum, Cardiff, Wales cf. p. 101 18c; F-M, 19c;

Headdress - Formal and Casual
Continental Europe

Boymans-van Beuningen Museum, Rotterdam, The Netherlands cf. p. 105 18c; A-M

Centraal Museum, Utrecht, The Netherlands cf. p. 105 17c; C, 18c; C, 19c; C-F-M, 20c; C-F

Groningen Museum voor Stad en Lande, Groningen, The Netherlands cf. p. 105 18c; F-M, 19c; F

Musée Alsaçien, Strasbourg, France cf. p. 103 U; F-M

Musée Bigouden, Pont-l'Abbé, France cf. p. 103 19c; F-M, 20c; F, U; F-M

Musée de la Vallée Noire, La Chatre, France cf. p. 102 U; F-M

Musée des Hautes-Alpes, Gap, France cf. p. 102 U; F-M

Musée du Costume de la ville de Paris, Paris, France cf. p. 102 16c; M, 17c; M, 18c; M

Musée du Donjon, Niort, France cf. p. 102 19c; F-M, 20c;

F-M, U; F-M

Musée Fontenille-Mondiére, Thiers, France cf. p. 103 19c; F-M

Musée Local de l'Art Provencal, Château-Gombert, France cf. p. 101 13c; F-M, 18c; C-F-M, 19c; C-F-M, 20c; C-F-M, U; C-F-M

Musée Normand d'Ethnographie et d'Art Populaire du Vieux-Honfleur, Honfleur, France cf. p. 102 18c; F

Musée Serret et de la Vallée de Saint-Amarin, Saint-Amarin, France cf. p. 103 U; F-M

Musées de Clermont-Ferrand: Musée des Beaux-Arts and Musée Historique, Clermont-Ferrand, France cf. p. 101 17c; F-M, 19c; F-M, 20c; F-M

Nederlands Kostuummuseum, The Hague, The Netherlands cf. p. 105 19c; F-M, 20c; F-M

Real Monasterio de las Hueglas, Burgos, Spain cf. p. 106 13c; M

Rijksmuseum, Amsterdam, The Netherlands cf. p. 105 18c; F

Rosenborg Castle, Copenhagen, Denmark cf. p. 101 17c; F-M, 19c; M

Headdress - Military
British Isles, United Kingdom

Armouries, London, England cf. p. 99 19c; M, 20c; M

Canongate Tolbooth Museum, Edinburgh, Scotland cf. p. 100 20c; M

Castle Museum, York, England cf. p. 100 17c; M, 18c; M, 19c; M, 20c; M, U; M

Castle, The, Carlisle, England cf. p. 98 18c; M

Huntley House Museum, Edinburgh, Scotland cf. p. 100 18c; M

Imperial War Museum, London, England cf. p. 99 20c; M

London Museum, London, England cf. p. 99 18c; M

Royal Welch Fusiliers, Caernarvon, Wales cf. p. 101 18c; M

Scottish United Services Museum, Edinburgh, Scotland cf. p. 100   18c; M, 19c; M, 20c; M

Headdress - Military
Continental Europe
Centraal Museum, Utrecht, The Netherlands   cf. p. 105   20c; M

Musée Fontenille-Mondière, Thiers, France   cf. p. 103 19c; M

Musée Normand d'Ethnographie et d'Art Populaire du Vieux-Honfleur, Honfleur, France cf. p. 102   U; M

Musée Paul Dupuy, Toulouse, France   cf. p. 103   18c; M, 19c; M

Musées de Clermont-Ferrand: Musée des Beaux-Arts and Musée Historique, Clermont-Ferrand, France   cf. p. 101 17c; M, 18c; M, 19c; M, 20c; M

Rijksmuseum, Amsterdam, The Netherlands   cf. p. 105   17c; M

Rosenborg Castle, Copenhagen, Denmark   cf. p. 101   17c; M

Vojni Muzej Jna, Beograd-Kalemegdan, Yugoslavia   cf. p. 107   19c; M, 20c; M

Historical Clothing - Austrian

Nineteenth Century
Court seal guard's clothing:
Vojni Muzej Jna, Beograd-
Kalemegdan, Yugoslavia

Twentieth Century
Croatian clothing: Vojni Muzej
Jna, Beograd-Kalemegdan,
Yugoslavia - Worn by the
Mayor of the town of Osijek
while it was under Austrian
rule

Unclassified
Royal livery of the Monarchies:
Kunsthistorisches Museum,
Vienna, Austria

Historical Clothing - British

Twelfth Century
Becket, Thomas A. (Archbishop
of Canterbury): Cathedral of
Saint-Stephen, Sens, France

Thirteenth Century
Boniface VIII: Monumenti Musei
e Gallerie Pontificie, Rome,
Italy - English embroidered
chasuble

Museo Sacro de Biblioteca
Vaticano, Rome, Italy - Alb
and English embroidered
chasuble
First Earl of Pembroke: City
of Glasgow Corporation Art
Gallery and Museum, Glasgow,
Scotland - His armor
was made in Greenwich for
man and horse

Fifteenth Century
Richard III: Warwick Castle Museum, Warwick, England -

His armor

Sixteenth Century
Helen, Duchess of Northumber-
land: Albury Park House, Guildford, England - Coronation robe
worn at the coronation of Queen
Elizabeth
Queen Elizabeth: Hatfield House,
Hatfield, England - A pair of
silk stockings which were the
first she had seen or worn, a
pair of gloves, and a garden
hat

Seventeenth Century
Charles I (m. Henrietta Maria
of France): London Museum,
London, England - Knitted silk
vest
Cordiners (Shoemaker's) Guild:
Huntley House Museum, Edin-
burgh, Scotland - Armor
Cromwellian cuirassier's helmet:
London Museum, London, Eng-
land
Dymoke Armor: London Museum,
London, England - Worn by the
King's Champion
Green Howards (Part of the York-
shire Regiments): Castle Museum,
York, England - Their military
clothing and accessories
King's Champion's armor: London
Museum, London, England -
Dymoke Armor
King William III (formerly William,
Prince of Orange, The Nether-
lands; m. Mary Stuart, daughter
of James II of England): Rijks-
museum, Amsterdam, The Nether-
lands - Shirt

Royal Welch Fusiliers, Caernarvon, Wales - Hat ribbon worn by
King William in 1690

Pikeman's armor: London Museum, London, England

Scottish Highlander costumes: Collection of J. Telfer Dunbar, Edinburgh, Scotland

Shoemaker's Guild Armor (known as the Cordiners Guild): Huntley House Museum, Edinburgh, Scotland

Yorkshire Militia: Castle Museum, York, England - Military clothing and accessories

Yorkshire Regiments: Castle Museum, York, England - Military clothing and accessories

Yorkshire Volunteers: Castle Museum, York, England - Military clothing and accessories

Yorkshire Yeomanry: Castle Museum, York, England - Military clothing and accessories

Eighteenth Century

British Navy: National Maritime Museum, London, England - Uniform

Duke of Wellington's Regiment: Castle Museum, York, England - Military clothing and accessories

Green Howards of the Yorkshire Regiment: Castle Museum, York, England - Military clothing and accessories

Grenadier's uniform: London Museum, London, England - Cap

Herald's tabard: Huntley House Museum, Edinburgh, Scotland

Queen's Household Cavalry: Castle Museum, York, England - Uniforms and armor

Royal Artillery uniforms: Laing Art Gallery and Museum, Newcastle-upon-Tyne, England

Royal Marines: National Maritime Museum, London, England - Military clothing

Scottish Highlander costumes: Collection of J. Telfer Dunbar, Edinburgh, Scotland

Volunteer Regiment: Huntley House Museum, Edinburgh, Scotland - Helmets

Yorkshire Militia: Castle Museum, York, England - Military clothing and accessories

Yorkshire Regiment: Castle Museum, York, England - Military clothing and accessories

Yorkshire Volunteers: Castle Museum, York, England - Military clothing and accessories

Yorkshire Yeomanry: Castle Museum, York, England - Military clothing and accessories

Nineteenth Century

Academic robes: Welsh Folk Museum, Cardiff, Wales

Assistant to the Lord Provost: Huntley House Museum, Edinburgh, Scotland - Uniform of red with white ermine collar; also, known as the Baillie uniform

Baillie uniform: Huntley House Museum, Edinburgh, Scotland - Red with white ermine collar; also, known as the uniform of the Assistant to the Lord Provost

Boer War: Castle Museum, York, England - Military clothing

British Navy: National Maritime Museum, London, England - Uniforms

Civil Defense: Welsh Folk Museum, Cardiff, Wales - Uniforms

Crimean War: Castle Museum, York, England - Military clothing

Duke of Wellington (military leader and Prime Minister of England at one time): Wellington Museum, London, England - His uniforms

Duke of Wellington's Regiment: Castle Museum, York, England - Military clothing and accessories

Duke of York's Own East Yorkshire Regiment: Castle Museum, York, England - Military clothing and accessories

East Yorkshire Regiment: Castle

Museum, York, England -
Military clothing and accessories
Herald's tabard: Guildhall Museum, London, England
Home Guards' uniforms: Welsh Folk Museum, Cardiff, Wales
King's Own Yorkshire Light Infantry: Castle Museum, York, England - Military clothing and accessories
Leed's Rifle Regiment: Castle Museum, York, England - Military clothing and accessories
Local Volunteers: Gallery of English Costume, Manchester, England - Uniforms
Lord Provost: Huntley House Museum, Edinburgh, Scotland - Civil uniform of red with white ermine collar and tuxedo front
Napoleonic Wars: Castle Museum, York, England - Military clothing
Paisley shawls:
National Museum of Antiquities of Scotland, Edinburgh, Scotland
Paisley Museum and Art Gallery, Paisley, Scotland
Peer's Livery: Welsh Folk Museum, Cardiff, Wales
Police Judge: Huntley House Museum, Edinburgh, Scotland - Civil uniform
Prince of Wales' Own West Yorkshire Regiment: Castle Museum, York, England - Military clothing and accessories
Queen's Bodyguard: Huntley House Museum, Edinburgh, Scotland - Uniform
Queen's Own Yorkshire Dragoons: Castle Museum, York, England - Military clothing and accessories
Queen Victoria (m. Albert of Saxe-Coburg-Gotha in 1840): London Museum, London, England - Tunic and hat worn by Queen Victoria when reviewing her troops, and her going away dress

Museo del Palacio, Madrid, Spain - Queen Victoria's train
Red Cross uniforms: Welsh Folk Museum, Cardiff, Wales
Royal Marines: National Maritime Museum, London, England - Uniforms
Welsh militia and regiment: Welsh Folk Museum, Cardiff, Wales - Uniforms
West Yorkshire Regiment (known as the Prince of Wales' Own): Castle Museum, York, England - Military clothing and accessories
York and Lancaster Regiment: Castle Museum, York, England - Military clothing and accessories
Yorkshire Dragoons: Castle Museum, York, England - Military clothing and accessories
Yorkshire Hussars: Castle Museum, York, England - Military clothing and accessories
Yorkshire Light Infantry (known as the King's Own): Castle Museum, York, England - Military clothing and accessories
Yorkshire Militia: Castle Museum, York, England - Military clothing and accessories
Yorkshire Regiment: Castle Museum, York, England - Military clothing and accessories
Yorkshire Volunteers: Castle Museum, York, England - Military clothing and accessories
Yorkshire Yeomanry: Castle Museum, York, England - Military clothing and accessories

Twentieth Century
Academic robes: Welsh Folk Museum, Cardiff, Wales
British Navy: National Maritime Museum, London, England - Uniforms
Civil Defense uniforms:

142

143

York, England - Military clothing and accessories

Yorkshire Regiment: Castle Museum, York, England - Military clothing and accessories

Yorkshire Volunteers: Castle Museum, York, England - Military clothing and accessories

Yorkshire Yeomanry: Castle Museum, York, England - Military clothing and accessories

Unclassified

Artic and Antarctica: Scott Polar Research Institute, Cambridge, England - Expedition clothing

Baron of the Cinque Port: Deal Museum, Deal, England - Complete robe

Drum major's mace: Castle Museum, York, England

Ducal Parliament: Woburn Abbey, Bletchley, England - Robes

Knight of the Garter: Woburn Abbey, Bletchley, England - Robes

Leeds Rifles: Castle Museum, York, England - Busby hat

Peeress' ceremonial robes for state occasions, as coronations: Woburn Abbey, Bletchley, England

Royal Artillery: Laing Art Gallery and Museum, Newcastle-upon-Tyne, England - Military uniforms

Scottish Highlander: Canongate Tolbooth Museum, Edinburgh, Scotland

Collection of J. Telfer Dunbar, Edinburgh, Scotland - Costumes

Second Life Guards: Laing Art Gallery and Museum, Newcastle-upon-Tyne, England - Uniforms

Third Battalion: Castle Museum, York, England - Color belt

Yorkshire Regiment: Castle Museum, York, England - Military accessories--badges,

buttons, insignia, helmet plates, and belt buckles

West Palaeartic costumes: Worthing Museum and Art Gallery, Worthing, England

Historical Clothing - Danish

Seventeenth Century

Crown of the Absolute Kings: Rosenborg Castle, Copenhagen, Denmark - Used by the kings from Christian V to Christian VIII

King Christian IV (m. Anne Katharina of Brandenburg and Kirsten Munk): Rosenborg Castle, Copenhagen, Denmark - Clothing including his costumes as Knight of the Garter; coronation riding equipment which was black velvet, richly embroidered with gold, jewels, and pearls; jewelry and medallions; his blood-stained clothes from the naval battle of Kolberger Heide including a black velvet-brocade jerkin, a silk and gold brocade cap, and a shirt with lace border

King Christian V (m. Charlotte Amalie of Hesse-Cassel): Rosenborg Castle, Copenhagen, Denmark - Clothing which includes his coronation robes

Knight of the Order of the Garter: Rosenborg Castle, Copenhagen, Denmark - Oldest known robes; garter and insignia ornamented with pearls; insignia set with diamonds

Eighteenth Century

Crown of the queen: Rosenborg Castle, Copenhagen, Denmark

Jewels for a reigning queen: Rosenborg Castle, Copenhagen, Denmark

King Christian VII (m. Caroline Mathilde of Great Britain): Rosenborg Castle, Copenhagen, Denmark - His Royal Robes

Order "de l'union parfaite": Rosen-

borg Castle, Copenhagen,
Denmark - Insignia

Nineteenth Century
Horse Guard: Rosenborg Castle,
Copenhagen, Denmark - Uni-
form

King Christian IX (m. Louise
of Hesse-Cassel): Rosenborg
Castle, Copenhagen, Denmark
- His civilian clothes with his
well-known brown coat, and
his General's uniform and
great coat worn at Dybbol in
1864

King Frederik VI (m. Marie
Sophie Frederikke of Hesse-
Cassel): Rosenborg Castle,
Copenhagen, Denmark - His
coronation robes

King Frederik VII (m. Vilhelmine
Marie of Denmark, Mariane
of Mecklenburg, and Louise
Rasmussen the Countess Dan-
ner): Rosenborg Castle,
Copenhagen, Denmark - His
red Fez

Medallion of gold containing locks
of the King's and Queen's hair:
Rosenborg Castle, Copenhagen,
Denmark

Queen Caroline Amalie (formerly
Caroline Amalie of Slesvig-
Holstein-Augustenburg, second
wife of Christian VIII of Denmark): Rosenborg Castle,
Copenhagen, Denmark - Her
silver-wedding handkerchief

Queen Vilhelmine Marie (was
Vilhelmine Marie of Denmark,
first wife of Frederik VII of
Denmark): Rosenborg Castle,
Copenhagen, Denmark - Her
engagement ring

Westphalian Crown Order: Rosenborg Castle, Copenhagen, Denmark - Insignia and star

Historical Clothing - Dutch

Fourteenth Century
Bishop's mitre and gloves: Centraal Museum, Utrecht, The

Netherlands

Seventeenth Century
Frederik Hendrik, Stadhonder:
Rijksmuseum, Amsterdam, The
Netherlands - Armorial coat
used at his funeral in 1647

Hendrik Casimir (nephew of Prince
Maurits of Orange): Rijksmuseum,
Amsterdam, The Netherlands -
Clothing and hat including his
mantel and pants

Eighteenth Century
Undertaker's hat: Groningen Mu-
seum voor Stad en Lande,
Groningen, The Netherlands

Nineteenth Century
Citizen Soldiery of Hoorn: West-
fries Museum, Hoorn, The
Netherlands - Uniforms

Citizen Soldiery of 's-Hertogenbosch:
Central North Brabant Museum,
's-Hertogenbosch, The Netherlands - Clothing

Police of Hoorn: Westfries Museum, Hoorn, The Netherlands
- Uniforms

Postal Officers: Musee Postal
Neerlandais, The Hague, The
Netherlands - Official uniforms

Twentieth Century
Artillery of the Utrecht Sharp-
shooters: Centraal Museum,
Utrecht, The Netherlands -
Clothing: tunics, trousers, and
hats

Knighthood of Utrecht: Centraal Museum, Utrecht, The Netherlands
- Dress uniforms including hats
and swords

Postal officers: Musee Postal Neerlandais, The Hague, The Netherlands - Official uniforms

Historical Clothing - French

Fifth Century
Golden jewelry discovered at Pouan
(Aube) in the burial place of a
barbarian chief, contemporary

with Attila: Musée des Beaux-Arts, Troyes, France

Thirteenth Century
Saint Bertrand: Cathedral, Saint-Bertrand-de-Comminges, France - Mitre

Fifteenth Century
Sister's habits: Hôtel-Dieu Museum, Beaune, France

Sixteenth Century
Mayor's uniforms: Musée du Costume de la ville de Paris, Paris, France
Sister's habits: Hôtel-Dieu Museum, Beaune, France
Tunics of the ancient crusaders: Musée du Louvre, Paris, France

Seventeenth Century
Mayor's uniforms: Musée du Costume de la ville de Paris, Paris, France
Sister's habits: Hôtel-Dieu Museum, Beaune, France

Eighteenth Century
Alsaçien Prince: Abbé de Murbach, Strasbourg, France - Clothing
Casual clothing of Damiens who struck Louis XV with a knife in 1757: Musée de l'Histoire de France, Paris, France
Judges' popular clothing including a cloak for summer and winter: Musée Normand d'Ethnographie et d'Art Populaire du Vieux-Honfleur, Honfleur, France
Mayor's uniforms: Musée du Costume de la ville de Paris, Paris, France
Queen Marie Antoinette: Wallace Collection, London, England - Necklace which was given to Princess de Lamballe
Sister's habits: Hôtel-Dieu Museum, Beaune, France

Nineteenth Century
Chimney sweep's costume: Musée Local de l'Art Provencal, Château-Gombert, France
Emperor Napoleon III: Museo del Risorgimento, Milan, Italy - Cloak, crown, and sceptre from the coronation of Napoleon as King of Italy

Stibbert Museum, Florence, Italy - Napoleon's coronation dress as King of Italy
French Zouave: Armeria Reale, Turin, Italy - Uniform which belonged to Victor Emanuel II, King of Italy, who received it from Napoleon III, Emperor of France, at the battle of Palestro (1859) during the war of the Italian Independence
Fortress guards: Musée Fontenille-Mondiere, Thiers, France - Uniform and hat
Marine uniforms: Musée de la Marine, Paris, France
Peasant headdress with "Montobaned" (foundation): Musée Bigouden, Pont-l'Abbé, France
Sister's habits: Hôtel-Dieu Museum, Beaune, France

Twentieth Century
Sister's habits: Hôtel-Dieu Museum, Beaune, France

Unclassified
Champagne region vineyard workers: Musée du Vin de Champagne, Épernay, France - Costumes
Collection of Cambodgiana clothing and jewelry: Musée de la Maison d'Ozé, Alençon, France
Costumes worn during the "Pardons" in the Cornouaille country of western Brittany: Musée des Arts Décoratifs et d'Art Populaire Régional, Nantes, France
Duke of Chartres: Musée de la Vénerie, Senlis, France - Hunting costume
Empress Eugenie: Musée de la Vénerie, Senlis, France - Hunt-

146

ing costume
Guilers headdress: Musée Bigou-
den, Pont-l'Abbé, France -
Named after the town in which
it was worn, also, a coiffe
bigouden
La Côte headdress: Musée
Bigouden, Pont-l'Abbé, France
- Named after the town in
which it was worn, also, a
coiffe bigouden
Marshal Berthier: Musée de la
Vénerie, Senlis, France -
Hunting costume
Mayors' uniforms: Musée du
Costume de la ville de Paris,
Paris, France
Merovingian jewelry: Musée
Danicourt, Péronne, France
"Miquelete" - a jacket which is
part of the costume of the
National Guard of d'Urrugne:
Musée Basque, Bayonne,
France
National Guard of d'Urrugne:
Musée Basque, Bayonne,
France - "Miquelete" jacket
which is part of their costume
Police of France: Musée de la
Préfecture de Police, Paris,
France - Uniforms from the
past and present
Pont-l'Abbé headdress: Musée
Bigouden, Pont-l'Abbé, France
- Named after the town in
which it was worn, also, a
coiffe bigouden
Sète water jousts: Musée
Municipal, Sète, France -
Costumes

Historical Clothing - German

Fifteenth Century
Gothic armor: Wallace Col-
lection, London, England -
Made from pieces from Italy
and Germany
Gothic war harness for horse
and man: Wallace Collection,
London, England

Sixteenth Century

Emperor Ferdinand I: Wallace
Collection, London, England
- Chanfron and vamplate from
part of an armor made for
Ferdinand I
Gothic armor: Wallace Collection,
London, England - Made from
pieces from Italy and Germany
Gothic crown from Germany:
Wallace Collection, London,
England
Gothic equestrian armor: Wallace
Collection, London, England
Otto Heinrich: Wallace Collection,
London, England - His equestrian
armor which had been made by
H. Ringler of Nuremberg

Seventeenth Century
Gothic armor: Wallace Collection,
London, England - Made of
pieces from Italy and Germany

Eighteenth Century
Burgermilitars (Old Hamburg City
Army): Museum für Hamburgische
Geschichte, Hamburg, Germany
- Uniforms
Gothic armor: Wallace Collection,
London, England
Old Hamburg City Army (known as
the Burgermilitars): Museum
für Hamburgische Geschichte,
Hamburg, Germany

Nineteenth Century
Burgermilitars (known as the Old
Hamburg City Army): Museum
für Hamburgische Geschichte,
Hamburg, Germany - Uniforms
Gogel (Minister of Finances under
King Louis Napoleon and King
William I): Rijksmuseum, Amster-
dam, The Netherlands - His
costume with insignia
Gothic armor: Wallace Collection,
London, England
Hanover Army: Bomann-Museum
Celle, Celle, Germany - Uni-
forms
Knights' uniforms: Bomann-Museum
Celle, Celle, Germany
Old Hamburg City Army (known as

Burgermilitars): Museum für
Hamburgische Geschichte,
Hamburg, Germany - Uniforms
Police uniforms: Bomann-Museum
Celle, Celle, Germany

Twentieth Century
Burgermilitars (known as Old
Hamburg City Army): Museum
für Hamburgische Geschichte,
Hamburg, Germany - Uni-
forms
Gothic armor: Wallace Collection,
London, England
Old Hamburg City Army (known
as Burgermilitars): Museum
für Hamburgische Geschichte,
Hamburg, Germany - Uni-
forms

Historical Clothing - Indian

Eighteenth Century
Iron helmet: Hermitage, Leningrad, Soviet Union - Lace-
carved, from India

Historical Clothing - Irish

Eighteenth Century
Herald's tabard: Genealogical
Office, Dublin, Ireland

Nineteenth Century
Herald's tabard: Genealogical
Office, Dublin, Ireland

Unclassified
Knight of the Order of St.
Patrick: Genealogical Office,
Dublin, Ireland - A robe

Historical Clothing - Italian

Fourteenth Century
Clement V: Cathedral, Saint-
Bertrand-de-Comminges,
France - Copes

Fifteenth Century
Gothic armor: Wallace Collection, London, England

Sixteenth Century

Gothic armor: Wallace Collection,
London, England

Seventeenth Century
Cuirassier armor: Wallace Col-
lection, London, England - Made
in Italy
Pontifical riding costume: Museo
Sacro de Biblioteca Vaticano,
Rome, Italy

Eighteenth Century
Drummer's uniforms in redcloth:
Museo Civico, Rieti, Italy
Pages' uniforms in redcloth:
Museo Civico, Rieti, Italy
Papal Guard of Rome: Historisches
Museum der Stadt Olten, Olten,
Switzerland - Uniform
Priori (high officials of the town):
Museo Civico, Rieti, Italy -
Black damask robes
Standard bearers: Museo Civico,
Rieti, Italy - Dress robe deco-
rated in gold and a small damask
and black silk umbrella decorated
with lace and gold fringe

Nineteenth Century
Napoleon: Museo del Risorgimento,
Milan, Italy - Cloak, crown and
sceptre from the coronation of
Napoleon as King of Naples, Italy

Stibbert Museum, Florence, Italy
- Coronation dress of Napoleon
as King of Italy

Unclassified
St. Ambrose: Museo della Basilica
di S. Ambrogio, Milan, Italy
- Dalmatic

Historical Clothing - Norwegian

Twentieth Century
Vicar: Norsk Folkemuseum, Oslo,
Norway - Robe

Historical Clothing - Portuguese

Fourteenth Century
Igreja da Ermida (Castro Daire):
Museu Nacional de Arte Antiga,

Lisbon, Portugal - Mitre

Sixteenth Century
Monastery of Jerónimos and
the Igreja de Graça, Lisbon:
Museu Nacional de Arte
Antiga, Lisbon, Portugal -
Church vestments from the
monastery

Seventeenth Century
Monastery of Jerónimos and
the Igreja da Graça, Lisbon:
Museu Nacional de Arte
Antiga, Lisbon, Portugal -
Church Vestments from the
monastery
Pluvial: Museu Nacional de
Arte Antiga, Lisbon, Portugal
- Velvet brocaded from the
Patriarchal Palace of Sao
Vicente

Eighteenth Century
Monastery of Jerónimos and the
Igreja da Graça, Lisbon:
Museu Nacional de Arte
Antiga, Lisbon, Portugal -
Church vestments from the
monastery

Historical Clothing - Russian
Fifth Century B. C.
Golden comb: Hermitage, Leningrad, Soviet Union - From the
Solokha barrow created with
figures of Scythians engaged
in battle

Fourteenth Century
Coronation robes: Armoury Museum, Moscow, Soviet Union

Historical Clothing - Serbian
Nineteenth Century
Serbian Army: Vojni Muzej Jna,
Beograd-Kalemegdan, Yugo-
slavia - Military clothing of
the army including solemn
blouses

Twentieth Century

Serbian Army: Vojni Muzej Jna,
Beograd-Kalemegdan, Yugo-
slavia - Military clothing from
the First World War

Historical Clothing - Siberian
Fourth Century B. C.
Siberian gold work: Hermitage,
Leningrad, Soviet Union - Neck-
rings, bracelets, and buckles

Historical Clothing - Spanish
Twelfth Century
King Alfonso: Museo del Palacio,
Madrid, Spain - His formal
clothing

Thirteenth Century
Monastic ceremonial robes: Real
Monasterio de las Hueglas,
Burgos, Spain - Robes of kings,
queens, and others

Fourteenth Century
Monastic ceremonial robes: Real
Monasterio de las Hueglas,
Burgos, Spain - Robes of kings,
queens, and others

Fifteenth Century
Monastic ceremonial robes: Real
Monasterio de las Hueglas,
Burgos, Spain - Robes of kings,
queens, and others
Queen Isabella: Catedral Museo,
Granada, Spain - Black church
robes worn by those bringing
Queen Isabella's body to Granada

Sixteenth Century
Monastic ceremonial robes: Real
Monasterio de las Hueglas,
Burgos, Spain - Robes of kings,
queens, and others

Seventeenth Century
Monastic ceremonial robes: Real
Monasterio de las Hueglas,
Burgos, Spain - Robes of kings,
queens, and others

Eighteenth Century

Bishop: Palacio Real Museo,
Madrid, Spain - Costume
Cardinal: Palacio Real Museo,
Madrid, Spain - Costume
King Charles III: Palacio Real
Museo, Madrid, Spain -
Formal costume
Monastic ceremonial robes: Real
Monasterio de las Hueglas,
Burgos, Spain - Robes of
kings, queens, and others
Spanish Order: Palacio Real
Museo, Madrid, Spain - Royal
clothing

Nineteenth Century
Announcer's costume worn at
bullfights: Museo Municipal
Taurino y de Artes Típicas,
Córdoba, Spain - Full knee
pants, tricorne hat, and shirt
with ruffles at neck and
sleeves
Bullfighting costumes: Museo
Municipal Taurino y de Artes
Típicas, Córdoba, Spain -
Includes those of the matador,
pickador and announcer
Matadors' bullfighting costumes:
Museo Municipal Taurino y
de Artes Típicas, Córdoba,
Spain - With pink hose, red
cape, red tie, and red cumberbund
Monastic ceremonial robes: Real
Monasterio de las Hueglas,
Burgos, Spain - Ceremonial
robes of kings, queens, and
others
Pickador's bullfighting costumes:
Museo Municipal Taurino y
de Artes Típicas, Córdoba,
Spain - With leather knee pants,
buttons down the side, black
cumberbund, long black tie,
gray felt broad-brimmed hat
with black rosette, and leather
knee boots

Twentieth Century
Announcer's costume for a bull-
fight: Museo Municipal
Taurino y de Artes Típicas,

Córdoba, Spain - With full knee
pants, tricorne hat, and shirt
with ruffles at neck and sleeves
Bullfighting costumes: Museo
Municipal Taurino y de Artes
Típicas, Córdoba, Spain - In-
cludes those of the matador,
pickador, and announcer
Matadors' bullfighting costumes:
Museo Municipal Taurino y de
Artes Típicas, Córdoba, Spain
- With pink hose, red cape,
red tie, and red cumberbund
Monastic ceremonial robes: Real
Monasterio de las Hueglas,
Burgos, Spain - Robes of kings,
queens, and others
Pickadors' bullfighting costumes:
Museo Municipal Taurino y de
Artes Típicas, Córdoba, Spain
- With leather knee
pants with buttons down the side,
black cumberbund, long black
tie, gray felt broadbrimmed hat
with black rosette, and leather
knee boots

Unclassified
Announcer's costume: Museo Taurino,
Madrid, Spain - For bullfights
Bullfighting costumes: Museo Tau-
rino, Madrid, Spain - Includes
those of the matador, pickador,
and announcer
Matador: Museo Taurino, Madrid,
Spain - Bullfighting costume
Pickador: Museo Taurino, Madrid,
Spain - Bullfighting costume

Historical Clothing - Swedish

Sixteenth Century
Coronation mantels: Kungl. Livrustkammaren, Stockholm, Sweden
Royal clothing: Nordiska Museet
und Skansen, Stockholm, Sweden

Seventeenth Century
Admiral Claes Bielkenstierna:
Kungl. Livrustkammaren, Stock-
holm, Sweden - Military clothing
Coronation mantels: Kungl. Livrust-
kammaren, Stockholm, Sweden

King Charles X Gustavus: Kungl. Livrustkammaren, Stockholm, Sweden - Casual and formal clothing

King Charles XI: Kungl. Livrustkammaren, Stockholm, Sweden - Casual and formal clothing

King Gustavus Adolphus: Kungl. Livrustkammaren, Stockholm, Sweden - Military clothing

Queen Christina: Kungl. Livrustkammaren, Stockholm, Sweden - Her clothing as a child

Eighteenth Century

Coronation mantels: Kungl. Livrustkammaren, Stockholm, Sweden

King Adolph Frederic: Kungl. Livrustkammaren, Stockholm, Sweden - Casual and formal clothing

King Charles XII: Kungl. Livrustkammaren, Stockholm, Sweden - Military clothing

King Charles XIII: Kungl. Livrustkammaren, Stockholm, Sweden - Military clothing

King Charles XIV (known as Bernadotte): Kungl. Livrustkammaren, Stockholm, Sweden - Military clothing

King Frederic I: Kungl. Livrustkammaren, Stockholm, Sweden - Military clothing

King Gustavus III: Kungl. Livrustkammaren, Stockholm, Sweden - Military clothing

King Gustavus IV Adolphus: Kungl. Livrustkammaren, Stockholm, Sweden - Military clothing and his clothing as a child

Lord High Chancellor: Nordiska Museet und Skansen, Stockholm, Sweden - Ceremonial costume

Prince Frederic Adolph: Kungl. Livrustkammaren, Stockholm, Sweden - Casual and formal clothing

Prince Gustavus: Kungl. Livrustkammaren, Stockholm,

Sweden - Military clothing and some of his clothing as a child

Princess Sophia Albertina: Kungl. Livrustkammaren, Stockholm, Sweden - Casual and formal clothing

Queen Desiree: Kungl. Livrustkammaren, Stockholm, Sweden - Casual and formal clothing

Queen Frederica: Kungl. Livrustkammaren, Stockholm, Sweden - Casual and formal clothing

Queen Hedwig: Kungl. Livrustkammaren, Stockholm, Sweden - Casual and formal clothing

Queen Louisa Ulrica: Kungl. Livrustkammaren, Stockholm, Sweden - Casual and formal clothing

Queen Sophia Magdalena: Kungl. Livrustkammaren, Stockholm, Sweden - Casual and formal clothing

Nineteenth Century

Coronation mantles: Kungl. Husgerådskammaren, Stockholm, Sweden

King Charles XIII: Kungl. Livrustkammaren, Stockholm, Sweden - Military clothing

King Charles XIV (known as Bernadotte): Kungl. Livrustkammaren, Stockholm, Sweden - Military clothing

King Charles XV: Kungl. Livrustkammaren, Stockholm, Sweden - Military clothing

King Gustavus IV Adolphus: Kungl. Livrustkammaren, Stockholm, Sweden - Military clothing

King Gustavus V: Kungl. Livrustkammaren, Stockholm, Sweden - Military clothing and some of his clothing as a child

King Oscar I: Kungl. Livrustkammaren, Stockholm, Sweden - Military clothing

King Oscar II: Kungl. Livrustkammaren, Stockholm, Sweden - Military clothing

Prince Frederic Adolph: Kungl. Livrustkammaren, Stockholm,

Sweden - Casual and formal clothing
Prince Gustavus (1799-1877): Kungl. Livrustkammaren, Stockholm, Sweden - Military clothing and some of his clothing as a child
Prince Gustavus (1827-1852): Kungl. Livrustkammaren, Stockholm, Sweden - Casual and formal clothing
Princess Eugenie: Kungl. Livrustkammaren, Stockholm, Sweden - Casual and formal clothing
Princess Sophia Albertina: Kungl. Livrustkammaren, Stockholm, Sweden - Casual and formal clothing
Queen Desiree: Kungl. Livrustkammaren, Stockholm, Sweden - Casual and formal clothing
Queen Frederica: Kungl. Livrustkammaren, Stockholm, Sweden - Casual and formal clothing
Queen Hedwig: Kungl. Livrustkammaren, Stockholm, Sweden - Casual and formal clothing
Queen Josephine: Kungl. Livrustkammaren, Stockholm, Sweden - Casual and formal clothing
Queen Sophia: Kungl. Livrustkammaren, Stockholm, Sweden - Casual and formal clothing
Queen Sophia Magdalena: Kungl. Livrustkammaren, Stockholm, Sweden - Casual and formal clothing
Queen Victoria: Kungl. Livrustkammaren, Stockholm, Sweden - Casual and formal clothing

Twentieth Century
Coronation mantels: Kungl. Husgeradskammaren, Stockholm, Sweden
King Gustavus V: Kungl. Livrustkammaren, Stockholm, Sweden - Military clothing
King Oscar II: Kungl. Livrustkammaren, Stockholm, Sweden

- Military clothing
Queen Sophia: Kungl. Livrustkammaren, Stockholm, Sweden - Casual and formal clothing
Queen Victoria: Kungl. Livrustkammaren, Stockholm, Sweden - Casual and formal clothing

Historical Clothing - Swiss

Eighteenth Century
Swiss Guards: Historisches Museum der Stadt Olten, Olten, Switzerland - Uniforms

Historical Clothing - Yugoslavian

Seventeenth Century
Magistrates of the Republic: Dubrovački Muzej, Dubrovnik, Yugoslavia - Open robes
Rectors of the Republic: Dubrovački Muzej, Dubrovnik, Yugoslavia - Official robes which had a black strip falling from the left shoulder
Small Council: Dubrovački Muzej, Dubrovnik, Yugoslavia - Official robes of the members

Eighteenth Century
Magistrates of the Republic: Dubrovački Muzej, Dubrovnik, Yugoslavia - Official robes
Patrician S. Gradie (Gradi): Dubrovački Muzej, Dubrovnik, Yugoslavia - Casual clothing
Patrician N. Pucie (Pozza): Dubrovački Muzej, Dubrovnik, Yugoslavia - Casual clothing
Patrician Sorkocevic: Dubrovački Muzej, Dubrovnik, Yugoslavia - Wallet

Nineteenth Century
Clothing for heroic dance named "Moreska" which originated in the sixteenth century in the province of Dalmatia on the island of Korcula: Vojni Muzej Jna, Beograd-Kalemegdan, Yugoslavia

Twentieth Century

Army of Yugoslavia: Vojni Muzej
Jna, Beograd-Kalemegdan,
Yugoslavia - Military clothing
of World War I and World War
II
Diplomatic dresscoat: Vojni
Muzej Jna, Beograd-Kalemeg-
dan, Yugoslavia - Worn
during the period between the
two World Wars
Infantry of Yugoslavia: Vojni
Muzej Jna, Beograd-Kalemeg-
dan, Yugoslavia - Uniforms
worn during the two World
Wars
Navy of Yugoslavia: Vojni Muzej
Jan, Beograd-Kalemegdan,
Yugoslavia - Uniforms worn
during the two World Wars
Royal Guard: Vojni Muzej Jna,
Beograd-Kalemegdan, Yugo-
slavia - Uniforms worn
during the two World Wars

Jewelry

Jewelry Code

c - Century
F - Female
M - Male
U - Unclassified as to century

Jewelry
British Isles, United Kingdom

Bignor Roman Villa Collection, Bignor, England cf. p. 98 U; F

Birmingham City Museum and Art Gallery, Birmingham, England cf. p. 98 U; F-M

Bowes Museum, Barnard Castle, England cf. p. 98 U; F-M

Castle Museum, York, England cf. p. 100 19c; F-M, 20c; F

County Museum, Carmarthen, Wales cf. p. 101 U; F-M

London Museum, London, England cf. p. 99 15c; F-M, 18c; F

Rotherham Museum and Art Gallery, Rotherham, England cf. p. 100 U; F-M

Wallace Collection, London, England cf. p. 99 15c; F-M, 16c; F-M, 18c; F, 19c; F

Worthing Museum and Art Gallery, Worthing, England cf. p. 100 U; F-M

Jewelry
Continental Europe

Bibliothèque Nationale, Paris, France cf. p. 102 U; F-M

Centraal Museum, Utrecht, The Netherlands cf. p. 105 18c; F, 19c; F, 20c; F

Central North Brabant Museum, 's-Hertogenbosch, The Netherlands cf. p. 105 16c; F, U; F

Dubrovački Muzej, Dubrovnik, Yugoslavia cf. p. 107 18c; F-M

Hermitage, Leningrad, Soviet Union cf. p. 106 1800 B. C. - 5 B. C.; F-M, 6 B. C.; F-M, 5 B. C.; F-M, 4 B. C.; F-M, 3 B. C.; F-M, 2 B. C.; F-M, 1 B. C.; F-M, 1c; F-M, 2c; F-M, 3c; F-M, 4c; F-M, 5c; F-M, 6c; F-M, 7c; F-M, 8c; F-M, 9c; F-M, 16c; F-M, 17c; F-M, 18c; F-M, 19c; F-M, 20c; F-M

Lázaro Galdiano Museum, Madrid, Spain cf. p. 106 U; F-M

Musée Crozatier, Le Puy-en-Velay, France cf. p. 102 U; F-M

Musée Danicourt, Péronne, France cf. p. 103 U; F-M

Musée de la Maison d'Ozé, Alençon, France cf. p. 101 U; F-M

Musée de la Princerie, Verdun, France cf. p. 103 U; F-M

Musées des Antiquités Nationales, Saint-German-en-Laye, France cf. p. 103 U; F-M

Musée des Beaux-Arts, Le Mans, France cf. p. 102 U; F-M

Musée des Beaux-Arts, Troyes, France cf. p. 103 U; F-M

Musée Masséna, Nice, France cf. p. 102 U; F-M

Musée Municipal, Agen, France cf. p. 101 U; F-M

Musée Préhistorique, Carnac, France cf. p. 101 U; F-M

Musée Régional, Sarrebourg,

France   cf. p. 103   U; F-M
Musée Saint-Raymond, Toulouse,
France   cf. p. 103   U; F-M
Rijksmuseum voor Völkskunde,
Arnhem, The Netherlands
cf. p. 105   16c; F-M
Rosenborg Castle, Copenhagen,
Denmark   cf. p. 101   16c;
F-M, 17c; F-M, 18c; F-M,
19c; F-M, U; F-M

Military Uniforms and Accessories

Military Uniforms and Accessory Code

c - Century
F - Female
M - Male
U - Unclassified as to century

Military Uniforms and Accessories

Continental Europe

Armeria Reale, Turin, Italy cf. p. 105 19c; M

Armoury Museum, Moscow, Soviet Union cf. p. 106 17c; M

Bomann-Museum Celle; Celle, Germany cf. p. 104 19c; M

Centraal Museum, Utrecht, The Netherlands cf. p. 105 20c; M

Central North Brabant Museum, 's-Hertogenbosch, The Netherlands cf. p. 105 19c; M

Groningen Museum voor Stad en Lande, Groningen, The Netherlands cf. p. 105 19c; M

Heeresgeschichtliches Museum, Vienna, Austria cf. p. 97 16c; M, 17c; M, 18c; M, 19c; M, 20c; M

Het Nederlands Leger-en Wapenmuseum "Generaal Hoefer," Leyden, The Netherlands cf. p. 105 U; M

Historisches Museum der Stadt Olten, Olten, Switzerland cf. p. 107 18c; M, 19c; M, 20c; M

Jämtlands Läns Museum, Östersund, Sweden cf. p. 106 19c; M, 20c; M

Kungl. Armémuseum, Stockholm, Sweden cf. p. 106 17c; M, 18c; M, 19c; M, 20c; M

Kungl. Livrustkammaren, Stockholm, Sweden cf. p. 107 16c; M, 17c; M, 18c; M, 19c; M, 20c; M

Kunsthistorisches Museum, Vienna, Austria cf. p. 97 U; M

Militarmuseum, Fort Kronan, Sweden cf. p. 106 U; M

Musée Basque, Bayonne, France cf. p. 101 U; M

Musée de la Marine, Paris, France cf. p. 103 19c; M

Musée de l'Armée, Paris, France cf. p. 102 17c; M, 18c; M, 19c; M

Musée de l'Histoire de France, Paris, France cf. p. 103 19c; M

Musée Fontenille-Mondiére, Thiers, France cf. p. 103 19c; M

Musée Historique, Mulhouse, France cf. p. 102 18c; M, 19c; M

Musée Historique, Strasbourg, France cf. p. 103 18c; F-M, 19c; F-M, 20c; F-M

Musée Militaire, Fontainebleau, France cf. p. 102 18c; M, 19c; M

Musée Normand d'Ethnographie et d'Art Populaire du Vieux-Honfleur, Honfleur, France cf. p. 102 18c; M, U; M

Musée Paul Dupuy, Toulouse, France cf. p. 103 18c; M, 19c; M

Musée Postal Neerlandais, The Hague, The Netherlands cf. p. 105 19c; M

Museo del Ejército, Madrid,
Spain cf. p.106 U; M
Museo del Palacio, Madrid,
Spain cf. p.106 20c; M
Museo del Risorgimento,
Venice, Italy cf. p.105 19c;
M
Museo Municipal Textil Biosca,
Tarrasa, Spain cf. p.106
U; M
Museo Naval, Milan, Italy
cf. p.104 U; M
Museo Storico Navale, Venice,
Italy cf. p.105 18c; M,
19c; M, 20c; M
Museum de Waag, Deventer,
The Netherlands cf. p.105
19c; M
Museum für Hamburgische
Geschichte, Hamburg, Ger-
many cf. p.104 18c; M,
19c; M, 20c; M
Muzeum Historyczne Miasta
Krakówa, Kraków, Poland
cf. p.105 U; M
Nederlandsch Historisch Scheep-
vaart Museum, Amsterdam,
The Netherlands cf. p.105
U; M
Nordiska Museet und Skansen,
Stockholm, Sweden cf. p.
107 16c; M, 17c; M, 18c;
M, 19c; M, 20c; M
Rijksmuseum, Amsterdam, The
Netherlands cf. p.105 17c;
M, 19c; M
Rosenborg Castle, Copenhagen,
Denmark cf. p.101 17c;
M, 19c; M, 20c; M
Vojni Muzej Jna, Beograd-
Kalemegdan, Yugoslavia cf.
p.107 18c; M, 19c; M, 20c;
M
Westfries Museum, Hoorn, The
Netherlands cf. p.105 19c;
M

Military Uniforms and Acces-
sories
  British Isles, Ireland
Ard-Mhúsaem Na h-Eireann,
Dublin, Ireland cf. p.97
18c; M, 19c; M

Military Uniforms and Accessories
  British Isles, United Kingdom
Armagh County Museum, Armagh,
Northern Ireland cf. p.100
U; M
Armouries, London, England cf.
p.99 19c; M, 20c; M
Borough Museum Collections,
Abingdon, England cf. p.98
U; M
Bradford City Art Gallery and
Museum, Bradford, England
cf. p.98 19c; F-M
Canongate Tolbooth Museum, Edin-
burgh, Scotland cf. p.100 20c;
M
Castle Museum, York, England
cf. p.100 17c; M, 18c; M,
19c; M, 20c; M, U; M
Castle, The, Carlisle, England
cf. p.98 18c; M, 19c; M, 20c;
M
Dorset Military Museum, Dorches-
ter, England cf. p.98 17c; M
18c; M, 19c; M, 20c; M
Gallery of English Costumes, Man-
chester, England cf. p.100
19c; F-M, 20c; F-M
Gorey Castle Museum, Jersey,
England cf. p.99 U; M
Hatfield House, Hatfield, England
cf. p.99 17c; M
Herefordshire Light Infantry Regi-
mental Museum, Hereford, Eng-
land cf. p.99 U; M
Huntley House Museum, Edinburgh,
Scotland cf. p.100 18c; M
Imperial War Museum, London,
England cf. p.99 20c; F-M
King's Own Regimental Museum,
Lancaster, England cf. p.99
U; M
Laing Art Gallery and Museum,
Newcastle-upon-Tyne, England
cf. p.100 18c; M, U; M
Londesborough Barracks, Hull,
England cf. p.99 U; M
London Irish Rifles Museum,
London, England cf. p.99
U; M
London Museum, London, England
cf. p.99 16c; M, 17c; M, 18c;
M, 19c; F-M

157

Museum of Childhood and Costume,
Blithfield, England   cf. p. 98
18c; M, 19c; M
National Army Museum, Camber-
ley, England   cf. p. 98   18c;
M, 19c; M, 20c; M
National Maritime Museum, Lon-
don, England   cf. p. 99   18c;
F-M, 19c; F-M, 20c; F-M
National Museum of Antiquities
of Scotland, Edinburgh, Scot-
land   cf. p. 100   U; M
Regimental Museum, Newcastle-
upon-Tyne, England   cf. p.
100 U; M
Royal Welch Fusiliers, Caernar-
von, Wales   cf. p. 101   18c;
M, 20c; M
Scottish United Services Mu-
seum, Edinburgh, Scotland
cf. p. 100   18c; M, 19c; M,
20c; M
Wallace Collection, London,
England   cf. p. 99   19c; M,
20c; M
Wellington Museum, London,
England   cf. p. 99   U; M
Welsh Folk Museum, Cardiff,
Wales   cf. p. 101   19c; M,
20c; M
Women's Royal Army Corps,
Lingfield, England   cf. p. 99
U; F

National and Regional Clothing
National and Regional Clothing Code

c	-	Century A.D.
B.C.	-	Century B.C.
A	-	Casual clothing
B	-	Formal clothing
C	-	Childrens' clothing
E	-	Ecclesiastical vestments
F	-	Female clothing
H	-	Headdress
J	-	Jewelry
M	-	Male clothing
N	-	National clothing
P	-	Professional uniforms
R	-	Regional clothing
S	-	Accessories
T	-	Civil uniforms
U	-	Unclassified as to century
X	-	Military clothing
Y	-	Armor
Z	-	Ceremonial clothing

National and Regional Clothing
African
Bernisches Historisches Museum, Bern, Switzerland cf. p. 107 U; A-B-F-M

Museum für Völkerkunde, Berlin, Germany cf. p. 103 U; A-B-F-M

Österreichisches Museum für angewandte Kunst, Vienna, Austria cf. p. 97 U; A-B-F-M

South African
British Museum, London, England cf. p. 99 U; H-M

White African
Musée de l'Homme, Paris, France cf. p. 103 17c; A-B-F-M, 18c; A-B-F-M, U; A-B-F-M

National and Regional Clothing
American - Central American
Musée de l'Homme, Paris, France cf. p. 103 17c; A-B-F-M, 18c; A-B-F-M, U; A-B-F-M

North American
Imperial War Museum, London, England cf. p. 99 20c; M-X

Musée de l'Homme, Paris, France cf. p. 103 17c; A-B-F-M, 18c; A-B-F-M, U; A-B-F-M

South American
British Museum, London, England cf. p. 99 U; F-S

Musée de l'Homme, Paris, France cf. p. 103 16c; A-B-F-M, 17c; A-B-F-M, 18c; A-B-F-M, U; A-B-F-M

Museum für Völkerkunde, Berlin, Germany cf. p. 103 U; A-B-F-M

National and Regional Clothing
Arabian
Catedral Museo, Granada, Spain cf. p. 106 15c; E-M

Chapelle Royale de Sainte-Anne,

159

Apt, France cf. p.101 U;
A-B-F-M
Asian, Central
Musée de l'Homme, Paris,
France cf. p.103 17c; A-B-
F-M, 18c; A-B-F-M, U; A-
B-F-M
Austrian
Burgenländisches Landesmuseum,
Eisenstadt, Austria cf. p.97
U; A-B-F-M
Heimatmuseum Egg, Vorarlberg,
Austria cf. p.97 U; A-B-
F-M
Kärntner Landesmuseum, Klagen-
furt, Austria cf. p.97 U;
A-B-F-M
Kunsthistorisches Museum,
Vienna, Austria cf. p.97
U; F-M-Z
Museo Storico Navale, Venice,
Italy cf. p.105 18c; M-X,
19c; M-X, 20c; M-X
Niederösterreichisches Landes-
museum, Vienna, Austria cf.
p.97 U; A-B-F-M
Öberosterreichisches Landes-
museum, Linz, Austria cf.
p.97 U; A-B-F-M
Österreichisches Museum für
Völkskunde, Vienna, Austria
cf. p.97 U; A-B-F-M
Österreichisches Museum für
angewandte Kunst, Vienna,
Austria cf. p.97 U; A-B-
F-M
Steirisches Völkskundemuseum,
Graz, Austria cf. p.97 U;
A-B-F-M
Tiroler Völkskunstmuseum,
Innsbruck, Austria cf. p.97
U; A-B-F-M
Völkskundliche Sammlung des
Salzburger Museums, Sals-
burg, Austria cf. p.97 U;
A-B-F-M
Vorarlberger Landesmuseum,
Bregenz, Austria cf. p.97
U; A-B-F-M
Belgian
Imperial War Museum, London,
England cf. p.99 20c; M-X
Brazilian

British Museum, London, England
cf. p.99 U; F-S
British
Bethnal Green Museum, London,
England cf. p.99 U; A-B-F-M
Castle Museum, York, England
cf. p.100 19c; H-M-S-X, 20c;
H-M-S-X
Gallery of English Costume, Man-
chester, England cf. p.100
19c; F-M-X, 20c; F-M-X
Victoria and Albert Museum, Lon-
don, England cf. p.99 17c;
A-B-M
Wallace Collection, London, Eng-
land cf. p.99 16c; H-M-S-Y
Chinese
Wallace Collection, London, Eng-
land cf. p.99 19c; H-M-S-Y
Dutch
Centraal Museum, Utrecht, The
Netherlands cf. p.105 20c;
M-T-X-Z
Central North Brabant Museum,
's-Hertogenbosch, The Nether-
lands cf. p.95 16c; A-F-J,
U; A-F-J
Fries Museum, Leeuwarden, The
Netherlands cf. p.95 U; A-B-
C-F-M
Het Nederlands Leger-en Wapen-
museum "Generaal Hoefer,"
Leyden, The Netherlands cf.
p.105 U; M-X
Rijksmuseum voor Völkskunde,
Arnhem, The Netherlands cf.
p.105 18c; A-B-C-F-M-Z, U;
A-B-F-M
Rijksmuseum Zuiderzeemuseum,
Enkhuizen, The Netherlands cf.
p.105 U; A-B-F-M
Westfries Museum, Hoorn, The
Netherlands cf. p.105 19c; M-
T-X
Zeeuws Museum, Middleburg, The
Netherlands cf. p.105 19c; A-
B-C-F-M-S-T, 20c; A-B-C-F-
M-S-T
Egyptian
British Museum, London, England
cf. p.99 5c; A-F-M, 6c; A-F-
M, 8c; A-F-M, 9c; A-F-M, 13c;
A-F-M

160

Château-Gombert, France cf.
p. 101 17c; A-M-S, 18c; A-B-
C-F-H-M, 19c; A-B-C-F-H-
M, 20c; C-F-H-M-S, U; A-B-
C-F-H-M-Z
Musée Maraichin, Croix-de-Vie,
France cf. p. 102 U; A-B-
F-M
Musée Préhistorique, Carnac,
France cf. p. 101 U; F-J-M
Musée Pyrénéen, Lourdes,
France cf. p. 102 U; A-B-
C-F-M
Musée Régional, Sarrebourg,
France cf. p. 103 U; F-J-M
Musée Régional Béarnais, Pau,
France cf. p. 103 19c; A-B-
F-M-Z, U; A-B-F-M
Musées de Clermont-Ferrand:
Musée des Beaux-Arts and
Musée Historique, Clermont-
Ferrand, France cf. p. 101
17c; A-B-F-H-M, 19c; A-B-
F-H-M, 20c; A-B-F-H-M
Musée Unterlinden, Colmar,
France cf. p. 101 U; A-B-
F-M
Permanent Exhibition of Corsi-
can Costumes, Corsica,
France cf. p. 101 U; A-B-
F-M
Victoria and Albert Museum,
London, England cf. p. 99
17c; F-M-S

German
Bayerisches Nationalmuseum,
Munich, Germany cf. p. 104
U; A-B-F-M
Bomann-Museum Celle, Celle,
Germany cf. p. 104 19c;
A-B-F-M-T-X-Z
Historisches Museum der Pfalz
mit Weinmuseum, Speyer,
Germany cf. p. 104 U; A-
B-F-M
Historisches Museum und Munz-
kabinett, Frankfurt am Main,
Germany cf. p. 104 U; A-
B-F-M
Museo Stibbert, Florence, Italy
cf. p. 104 15c; M-Y, 16c;
M-Y
Museum für Hamburgische

Geschichte, Hamburg, Germany
cf. p. 104 18c; M-X, 19c; M-
X, 20c; M-X
Museum für Völkerkunde und
Vorgeschichte, Hamburg, Ger-
many cf. p. 104 20c; A-B-F-
M, U; A-B-F-M
National Museum, Nürnberg, Ger-
many cf. p. 104 U; A-B-F-M
Wallace Collection, London, Eng-
land cf. p. 99 15c; H-M-Y,
16c; H-S-Y, 17c; M-S-Y, 18c;
H-M-Y, 19c; H-M-Y-Z, 20c;
M-S-Y

Greek
Hermitage, Leningrad, Soviet
Union cf. p. 106 7 B. C.; F-M
S, 6 B. C.; F-J-M-S, 5 B. C.;
F-J-M-S, 4 B. C.; F-J-M-S,
3 B. C.; F-J-M-S, 2 B. C.; F-J-
M-S, 1 B. C.; F-J-M-S, 1c; F-
J-M-S, 2c; F-J-M-S, 3c; F-J-
M-S, 4c; F-M-J-S

Hawaiian
Museum für Völkerkunde, Berlin,
Germany cf. p. 103 U; F-M-Z

Indian
Hermitage, Leningrad, Soviet
Union cf. p. 106 15c; M-Y,
16c; M-Y, 17c; M-Y, 18c; H-M-
Y
Museum für Völkerkunde, Berlin,
Germany cf. p. 103 19c; A-B-
F-M
Wallace Collection, London, Eng-
land cf. p. 99 18c; H-M-S-Y,
19c; H-M-S-Y, 20c; H-M, U;
M-Y

Indian-Bolivia
Museum für Völkerkunde, Berlin,
Germany cf. p. 103 U; A-B-
F-M

Indian-North America
Bernisches Historisches Museum,
Bern, Switzerland cf. p. 107
19c; A-B-F-M-S
Museum für Völkerkunde, Berlin,
Germany cf. p. 103 U; A-B-
F-M

Indian-Peru
British Museum, London, England
cf. p. 99 U; F-S
Museum für Völkerkunde, Berlin,

163

Musées de Clermont-Ferrand:
Musée des Beaux-Arts and
Musée Historique, Clermont-
Ferrand, France cf. p. 101
1c; A-F-S
Musée Municipal, Agen, France
cf. p. 101 U; H-M-Y
Russian
Armoury Museum, Moscow,
Soviet Union cf. p. 106
16c; A-B-M
Kungl. Livrustkammaren, Stock-
holm, Sweden cf. p. 107
18c; E-M, U; E-M
Scottish
Canongate Tolbooth Museum,
Edinburgh, Scotland cf. p.
100 U; A-B-F-M
Collection of J. Telfer Dunbar,
Edinburgh, Scotland cf. p.
100 17c; A-B-F-M, 18c;
A-B-F-M, U; A-B-F-M
Highland Folk Museum, Kin-
gussie, Scotland cf. p. 101
U; A-B-F-M
National Museum of Antiquities
of Scotland, Edinburgh, Scot-
land cf. p. 100 17c; A-B-
F-M, 18c; A-B-F-M, 20c;
A-B-F-M, U; A-B-F-M
Paisley Museum and Art Gal-
lery, Paisley, Scotland cf.
p. 101 19c; A-B-F
Scottish United Services Mu-
seum, Edinburgh, Scotland
cf. p. 100 18c; H-M-X, 19c;
H-M-X, 20c; H-M-X
Siberian
Hermitage, Leningrad, Soviet
Union cf. p. 106 4 B.C.;
F-J-M-S, 3 B.C.; F-J-M-
S, 2 B.C.; F-J-M-S
Spanish
Museo del Pueblo Español, Ma-
drid, Spain cf. p. 106 17c;
A-B-F-M, 18c; A-B-F-M,
19c; A-B-F-M, 20c; A-B-F-M
Museo del Traje Español, Ma-
drid, Spain cf. p. 106 U;
A-B-F-M
Museo Municipal Taurino y de
Artes Típicas, Córdoba, Spain
cf. p. 106 19c; A-B-H-M-P,

20c; A-B-H-M-P
Museo Nacional de Arte Antiga,
Lisbon, Portugal cf. p. 106
15c; E-M
Museo Taurino, Madrid, Spain
cf. p. 106 U; A-B-M-P
Swedish
Jämtlands Läns Museum, Öster-
sund, Sweden cf. p. 106 18c;
B-F-M, 19c; A-B-F-M-Z
Kulturhistoriska Museet, Lund,
Sweden cf. p. 106 18c; A-B-
F-M, 19c; A-B-F-M, 20c; A-
B-F-M, U; A-B-F-M
Kungl. Armémuseum, Stockholm,
Sweden cf. p. 106 17c; M-X,
18c; M-X, 19c; M-X, 20c; M-X
Kungl. Livrustkammaren, Stock-
holm, Sweden cf. p. 107 16c;
E-M
Nordiska Museet und Skansen,
Stockholm, Sweden cf. p. 107
16c; A-B-C-F-M, 17c; A-B-C-
F-M, 17c; F-M-X, 18c; A-B-C-
F-M, 18c; A-B-C-F-M-X, 19c;
A-B-C-F-M, 19c; F-M-X, 20c;
A-B-C-F-M, 20c; M-X
Swiss
Schweiz. Trachtenmuseum, Lucerne,
Switzerland cf. p. 107 U; A-B-
F-M
Turkish
Hermitage, Leningrad, Soviet
Union cf. p. 106 16c; F-J-M-Y,
17c; F-J-M-Y
Museum für Völkerkunde, Berlin,
Germany cf. p. 103 U; A-B-F-M
Wallace Collection, London, Eng-
land cf. p. 99 18c; M-S-Y, 19c;
M-S-Y
Welsh
Welsh Folk Museum, Cardiff, Wales
cf. p. 101 19c; A-C-F-M-T-X-
Z, 20c; A-M-T-X-Z
Yugoslavian
Dubrovački Muzej, Dubrovnik,
Yugoslavia cf. p. 107 17c; A-
B-F-M, 18c; A-B-F-M
Vojni Muzej Jna, Beograd-Kalemeg-
dan, Yugoslavia cf. p. 107 19c;
A-B-M-X, 20c; A-B-M-X

Professional Uniforms

British Isles, United Kingdom

Nineteenth Century
Women's professional clothing:
Bradford City Art Gallery and
Museums, Bradford, England

Twentieth Century
Police uniforms: Imperial War
Museum, London, England

Unclassified
Railroad uniforms: Railway Museum,
York, England

Continental Europe

Eighteenth Century
Undertaker's hat: Groningen
Museum voor Stad en Lande,
Groningen, The Netherlands

Nineteenth Century
Bullfighters' costumes including
those of the matador, pickador,
and announcer: Museo Municipal
Taurino y de Artes Típicas,
Córdoba, Spain
Police uniforms: Bomann-Museum
Celle, Celle, Germany
Postal officers' uniforms: Musée
Postal Neerlandais, The Hague,
The Netherlands

Twentieth Century
Bullfighters' costumes including
those of the matador, pickador,
and announcer: Museo Municipal
Taurino y de Artes Típicas,
Córdoba, Spain
Postal officers' uniforms: Musée
Postal Neerlandais, The Hague,
The Netherlands

Unclassified
Bullfighters' costumes including

those of the matador, pickador,
and announcer: Museo Taurino,
Madrid, Spain
Police uniforms of France: Musée
de la Préfecture de Police,
Paris, France
Water Jousts' costumes from Séte:
Musée Municipal, Séte, France

Clothing Terms

Europe

Accessories

Belts - Color of the 3rd Battalion: Castle Museum, York, England cf. p.100 U

Belts - Undress pouch: Castle Museum, York, England cf. p.100 U

Buttons - Jewelled: London Museum, London, England cf. p.99 16c

Collars - False or stiff: Musée Fontenille-Mondiére, Thiers, France cf. p.103 19c

Fans:

Boymans-van Beuningen Musem, Rotterdam, The Netherlands cf. p.105 20c

British Museum, London, England cf. p.99 13c

Castle Museum, York, England cf. p.100 19c

Centraal Museum, Utrecht, The Netherlands cf. p.105 18c; 19c; 20c

Dubrovački Muzej, Dubrovnik, Yugoslavia cf. p.107 18c

Groningen Museum voor Stad en Lande, Groningen, The Netherlands cf. p.105 19c

Laing Art Gallery and Museum, Newcastle-upon-Tyne, England cf. p.100 18c; 19c

London Museum, London, England cf. p.99 18c

Luton Museum and Art Gallery, Luton, England cf. p.100 19c; 20c

Musée du Costume de la ville de Paris, Paris, France cf. p.102 18c; 19c; 20c

Musée Local de l'Art Provencal, Château-Gombert, France cf. p.101 18c

Nederlandsch Historisch Scheepvaart Museum, Amsterdam, The Netherlands cf. p.105 U

Red House Museum and Art Gallery, Christchurch, England cf. p.98 18c; 19c

Rijksmuseum, Amsterdam, The Netherlands cf. p.105 18c

Victoria and Albert Museum, London, England cf. p.99 16c; 17c; 18c

Welsh Folk Museum, Cardiff, Wales cf. p.101 18c; 19c

Fichus:

London Museum, London, England cf. p.99 18c; 19c

Musée Local de l'Art Provencal, Château-Gombert, France cf. p.101 U

Girdles - Egyptian: British Museum, London, England cf. p.99 13c

Gloves - French: Victoria and Albert Museum, London, England cf. p.99 17c

Gloves - Formal: Armoury Museum, Moscow, Soviet Union cf. p.106 17c

Gloves - Men's: London Museum, London, England cf. p.99 16c

Gloves - Men's and women's: Victoria and Albert Museum, London, England cf. p.99 16c

Gloves - Queen Elizabeth's: Hatfield House, Hatfield, England cf. p.99 16c

Gloves - Spence collection of formal gloves: Guildhall Museum, London, England cf. p.99 16c; 19c

Handbags: London Museum, London, England cf. p.99 20c

Handbags - Purses: Museo Municipal Textil Biosca, Tarrasa, Spain

cf. p.106 16c; 17c; 18c
Handbags - Reticules:
Castle Museum, York, England cf. p.100 19c
London Museum, London, England cf. p.99 18c
Jabots: Musée du Donjon, Niort, France cf. p.102 19c; 20c
Lappets: Boymans-van Beuningen Museum, Rotterdam, The Netherlands cf. p.105 18c
Muffs - Fur:
Castle Museum, York, England cf. p.100 19c
Laing Art Gallery and Museum, Newcastle-upon-Tyne, England cf. p.100 18c; 19c
Muffs - Silk: Castle Museum, York, England cf. p.100 18c
Parasols:
Castle Museum, York, England cf. p.100 19c
Groningen Museum voor Stad en Lande, Groningen, The Netherlands cf. p.105 19c
Laing Art Gallery and Museum, Newcastle-upon-Tyne, England cf. p.100 19c
London Museum, London, England cf. p.99 19c; 20c
Luton Museum and Art Gallery, Luton, England cf. p.100 19c; 20c
Musée Local de l'Art Provencal, Château-Gombert, France cf. p.101 19c; 20c
Red House Museum and Art Gallery, Christchurch, England cf. p.98 19c
Pince-nez: Rosenborg Castle, Copenhagen, Denmark cf. p.101 17c
Ruffs: Boymans-van Beuningen Museum, Rotterdam, The Netherlands cf. p.105 18c
Supportasses: Victoria and Albert Museum, London, England cf. p.99 16c
Veils- Wedding: Boymans-van Beuningen Museum, Rotterdam, The Netherlands cf. p.105

20c
Walking sticks:
Dubrovački Muzej, Dubrovnik, Yugoslavia cf. p.107 18c
London Museum, London, England cf. p.99 18c
Musée du Costume de la ville de Paris, Paris, France cf. p.102 18c; 19c; 20c
Musée Local de l'Art Provencal, Château-Gombert, France cf. p.101 19c
Umbrellas:
Centraal Museum, Utrecht, The Netherlands cf. p.105 19c; 20c
Musée du Costume de la ville de Paris, Paris, France cf. p.102 19c; 20c

Armor
Armet: Wallace Collection, London, England cf. p.99 15c
Barbute-Italian: Wallace Collection, London, England cf. p.99 14c; 15c; 16c; 17c; 19c; 20c
Bascinet-Italian: Wallace Collection, London, England cf. p.99 14c
Besague: Wallace Collection, London, England cf. p.99 16c
Breastplates:
Castle Museum, York, England cf. p.100 17c
London Museum, London, England cf. p.99 16c
Musées de Clermont-Ferrand: Musée des Beaux-Arts and Musée Historique, Clermont-Ferrand, France cf. p.101 17c; 18c; 19c; 20c
Wallace Collection, London, England cf. p.99 16c
Breaths-part of armor through which one breathes: Wallace Collection, London, England cf. p.99 16c
Buckhurst suit-armor with the long peascod breast as seen in civilian clothing: Wallace Collection, London, England cf. p.99 16c
Burgonets:
London Museum, London, England cf. p.99 16c

167

Beaux-Arts and Musée Historique, Clermont-Ferrand, France cf. p. 101 1c

Stockings - Men's and women's: Victoria and Albert Museum, London, England cf. p. 99 16c

Stockings - Queen Elizabeth's Silk: Hatfield House, Hatfield, England cf. p. 99 16c

Headdress

Bonnets: Castle Museum, York, England cf. p. 100 19c

Caps - Embroidered: London Museum, London, England cf. p. 99 16c; 17c

Caps - Forage: Castle Museum, York, England cf. p. 100 19c; 20c

Caps - Knitted woolen: London Museum, London, England cf. p. 99 16c

Caps - Tweed: Castle Museum, York, England cf. p. 100 20c

Caps - Undress: Victoria and Albert Museum, London, England cf. p. 99 16c

Caps - Woolen: Guildhall Museum, London, England cf. p. 99 16c

Coifs: London Museum, London, England cf. p. 99 16c

Coifs - Ancient coifs of the Alpines:
Musée des Hautes-Alpes, Gap, France cf. p. 102 U
Musée du Donjon, Niort, France cf. p. 102 U

Coifs - Local: Musée Serret et de la Vallée de Saint-Amarin, Saint-Amarin, France cf. p. 103 U

Hats - Beaver: Castle Museum, York, England cf. p. 100 18c; 19c

Hats - Bicorn: Castle Museum, York, England cf. p. 100 18c

Hats - Calash: Castle Museum, York, England cf. p. 100 18c

Hats - Cocked: London Museum, London, England cf. p. 99 18c

Hats - Deerstalker: Castle Museum, York, England cf. p. 100 19c

Hats - Derby; black felt: Castle Museum, York, England cf. p. 100 20c

Hats - Fez; red, belonged to Frederik VII of Denmark: Rosenborg Castle, Copenhagen, Denmark cf. p. 101 19c

Hats - Garden: Hatfield House, Hatfield, England cf. p. 99 16c

Hats - Leghorn straw: Castle Museum, York, England cf. p. 100 18c

Hats - Pork die: Castle Museum, York, England cf. p. 100 19c

Hats - Straw boater: Castle Museum, York, England cf. p. 100 19c

Hats - Tam-o-shanter; silk: Castle Museum, York, England cf. p. 100 19c

Hats - Turban: Castle Museum, York, England cf. p. 100 18c

Wigs - Men's - Full bottomed: Castle Museum, York, England cf. p. 100 18c

Wigs - Men's - Powdered: Castle Museum, York, England cf. p. 100 18c

Wigs - Men's - Tricorne over bag: Castle Museum, York, England cf. p. 100 18c

Wigs - Women's - Egyptian women's real hair: British Museum, London, England cf. p. 99 13c

Jewelry

Caucasian jewelry: Hermitage, Leningrad, Soviet Union cf. p. 106 Bronze Age (18 B. C. through 1 B. C.); 1c through 9c

Crown - wedding: Musée Alsaçien, Strasbourg, France cf. p. 103 19c

Earrings - barbaric: Musée Saint-Raymond, Toulouse, France cf. p. 103 U

Ornaments - Bone and metal: Guildhall Museum, London, England cf. p. 99 1c through 18c

Ornaments - Ecclesiastical:

Musée Historique des Tissus,
Lyon, France cf. p.102
13c; 14c; 15c; 16c; 17c;
18c; 19c
Musée Lyonnais des Arts
Décoratifs, Lyon, France
cf, p.102 16c; 17c; 18c
Watch - pocket:
Dubrovački Muzej, Dubrovnik,
Yugoslavia cf. p.107 18c
Rosenborg Castle, Copenhagen,
Denmark cf. p.101 18c

Men's Clothing
Bikini-type leather trunks:
Guildhall Museum, London,
England cf. p.99 1 A.D.
Boleros - formal and casual:
Museo Municipal Textil
Biosca, Tarrasa, Spain cf.
p.106 18c
Breeches - Bucksin: London Mu-
seum, London, England cf.
p. 99 18c
Breeches - Knee:
Laing Art Gallery and Mu-
seum, Newcastle-upon-
Tyne, England cf. p.100
18c
London Museum, London,
England cf. p.99 17c;
18c
Victoria and Albert Museum,
London, England cf. p.99
17c; 18c
Welsh Folk Museum, Cardiff,
Wales cf. p.101 18c; 19c
Breeches - Petticoat:
Laing Art Gallery and Mu-
seum, Newcastle-upon-
Tyne, England cf. p.100
18c
London Museum, London,
England cf. p.99 17c; 18c
Victoria and Albert Museum,
London, England cf. p.99
17c; 18c
Welsh Folk Museum, Cardiff,
Wales cf. p.101 18c; 19c
Breeches - Riding:
Laing Art Gallery and Mu-
seum, Newcastle-upon-
Tyne, England cf. p.100

18c
London Museum, London, Eng-
land cf. p.99 17c; 18c
Victoria and Albert Museum,
London, England cf. p.99
17c; 18c
Welsh Folk Museum, Cardiff,
Wales cf. p.101 18c; 19c
Chemise:
Centraal Museum, Utrecht, The
Netherlands cf. p.105 17c
Musée Local de l'Art Provencal,
Château-Gombert, France
cf. p.101 19c
Coats - Buff: Wallace Collection,
London, England cf. p.99 17c
Coats - Riding: Victoria and Albert
Museum, London, England cf.
p.99 17c
Coats - Waistcoats:
London Museum, London, England
cf. p.99 17c; 18c; 19c; 20c
Victoria and Albert Museum,
London, England cf. p.99
17c; 18c; 19c; 20c
Doublets:
London Museum, London, Eng-
land cf. p.99 16c; 17c
Rijksmuseum, Amsterdam, The
Netherlands cf. p.105 17c
Doublets - "Peasecod" belly:
Victoria and Albert Museum,
London, England cf. p.99 17c
Jackets - Smoking: Castle Museum,
York, England cf. p.100 20c
Jerkin - Black velvet brocade:
Rosenborg Castle, Copenhagen,
Denmark cf. p.101 17c
Jerkin - Slashed leather: London
Museum, London, England cf.
p.99 16c
Lounge robe: Musée Local de l'Art
Provencal, Château-Gombert,
France cf. p.101 17c
Smocks - farmers': Red House Mu-
seum and Art Gallery, Christ-
church, England cf. p.98 18c;
19c
Suits - Men's lounge: London Mu-
seum, London, England cf. p.
99 20c
Suits - Men's tweed for town wear:
Castle Museum, York, England

172

173

and Museum, Newcastle-upon-Tyne, England cf. p.100 19c

Capes - Women's:
Centraal Museum, Utrecht, The Netherlands cf. p. 105 19c; 20c
Ard-Mhusaem Na h'Éireann, Dublin, Ireland cf. p.98 19c; 20c

Cloaks: Musée du Costume de la ville de Paris, Paris, France cf. p.102 20c

Cloaks - Grey slashed satin cloak embroidered in yellow silk: Victoria and Albert Museum, London, England cf. p.99 16c

Cloaks - Red with yellow applique work:
Victoria and Albert Museum, London, England cf. p. 99 16c

Cloaks: London Museum, London, England cf. p.99 16c

Coats - Caped overcoat: Castle Museum, York, England cf. p.100 19c

Coats - Driving: Victoria and Albert Museum, London, England cf. p.99 18c

Coats - Frock:
Castle Museum, York, England cf. p.100 19c
Laing Art Gallery and Museum, Newcastle-upon-Tyne, England cf. p.100 18c

Coats - General officer's: London Museum, London, England cf. p. 99 18c

Coats - Overcoat:
London Museum, London, England cf. p.99 19c; 20c
Nederlandsch Historisch Scheepvaart Museum, Amsterdam, The Netherlands cf. p.105 U

Coats - Riding: Victoria and Albert Museum, London, England cf. p.99 18c

Coats - Smoking: Museo Municipal Textil Biosca, Tarrasa, Spain cf. p.106 18c

Coats - Waistcoats:
Dubrovački Muzej, Dubrovnik, Yugoslavia cf. p.107 18c
Laing Art Gallery and Museum, Newcastle-upon-Tyne, England cf. p.100 18c; 19c
London Museum, London, England cf. p.99 18c; 19c
Musée Normand d'Ethnographie et d'Art Populaire du Vieux-Honfleur, Honfleur, France cf. p.102 18c; 19c
Musée Royaux d'Art et d'Histoire, Brussels, Belgium cf. p.98 18c; 19c
Victoria and Albert Museum, London, England cf. p.99 18c; 19c
Welsh Folk Museum, Cardiff, Wales cf. p.101 18c; 19c

Coatee: Castle Museum, York, England cf. p.100 19c

Jackets:
Castle Museum, York, England cf. p.100 19c
Musée Local de l'Art Provencal, Château-Gombert, France cf. p.101 17c

Mantles - Coronation: Kungl. Livrustkammaren, Stockholm, Sweden cf. p.107 16c

Mantles - Formal and casual men's: Musée Local de l'Art Provencal, Château-Gombert, France cf. p.101 17c

Mantles - Men's Formal and casual: and women's: Museo Municipal Textil Biosca, Tarrasa, Spain cf. p.106 17c

Mantles - Fur trimmed:
Castle Museum, York, England cf. p.100 19c
Red House Museum and Art Gallery, Christchurch, England cf. p.98 19c

Mantles - South American, made of plumes: Musée de l'Homme, Paris, France cf. p.103 16c

Mantles - Spanish style: Victoria and Albert Museum, London, England cf. p.99 18c

Mantlelets: Musée Bigouden, Pontl'Abbe, France cf. p.103 20c

174

Pelerines:
Castle Museum, York, England cf. p. 100 19c
Victoria and Albert Museum, London, England cf. p. 99 19c
Robes - Gallo-Roman: Musées de Clermont-Ferrand: Musée des Beaux-Arts and Musée Historique, Clermont-Ferrand, France cf. p. 101 1c
Shawls:
Centraal Museum, Utrecht, The Netherlands cf. p. 105 18c
Musée du Costume de la ville de Paris, Paris, France cf. p. 102 18c
Welsh Folk Museum, Cardiff, Wales cf. p. 101 18c
Tunics - Egyptian: British Museum, London, England cf. p. 99 5c; 6c

Women's Clothing
Buffon: Victoria and Albert Museum, London, England cf. p. 99 18c
Bustles:
Castle Museum, York, England cf. p. 100 19c
Musée Fontenille-Mondiére, Thiers, France cf. p. 103 19c
Victoria and Albert Museum, London, England cf. p. 99 16c; 19c
Caracos: Centraal Museum, Utrecht, The Netherlands cf. p. 105 18c
Coat dress:
Centraal Museum, Utrecht, The Netherlands cf. p. 105 19c
London Museum, London, England cf. p. 99 19c; 20c
Dresses - Bathing: London Museum, London, England cf. p. 99 20c
Dresses - Evening: London Museum, London, England cf. p. 99 20c
Dresses - Garden party: London Museum, London, England

cf. p. 99 20c
Dresses - Pannier: Castle Museum, York, England cf. p. 100 18c
Dresses - Sack-back:
Castle Museum, York, England cf. p. 100 18c
Victoria and Albert Museum, London, England cf. p. 99 18c
Dresses - Wedding:
Huntley House Museum, Edinburgh, Scotland cf. p. 100 19c
London Museum, London, England cf. p. 99 20c
Red House Museum and Art Gallery, Christchurch, England cf. p. 98 19c
Gowns: Armoury Museum, Moscow, Soviet Union cf. p. 106 17c
Panniers - linen covered and hinged: Castle Museum, York, England cf. p. 100 18c
Polonaise: Victoria and Albert Museum, London, England cf. p. 99 18c
Stomachers: London Museum, London, England cf. p. 99 17c
Tucker: Rosenborg Castle, Copenhagen, Denmark cf. p. 101 17c
Tunic - Queen Victoria's, worn when reviewing her troops: London Museum, London, England cf. p. 99 19c

175

DATE DUE

DATE DUE

| GAYLORD | | PRINTED IN U.S.A. |